Foreword

I welcome and value this sourcebook that has been based on experience and evidence gathered by One Plus One.

We have always known how important relationships are for the developing child and this has become more important recently as our understanding of neurological development expands. The presence of a loving and trusting relationship from the very beginning of a child's life lays the foundation for future health and well-being. Wider family relationships, especially those between the mother and father, are inevitably complicated and vulnerable to stressful events such as the birth of a child. For a developing child relationships matter and will have an enduring impact on a child's sense of self and the world around them.

In March 2008 we published the updated Child Health Promotion Programme (CHPP) for pregnancy and the first years of life. This update, which is based on the National Service Framework, recognises the importance of relationships in child health and well-being and places a greater emphasis on promoting positive relationships as part of the universal programme, as well as the 'progressive' additional elements for those families and children with additional needs and risks. The CHPP is one part of a portfolio of evidence based programmes and services that aim to provide mothers and fathers with the guidance and care to enable them to do the best for their child. The Family Nurse Partnership is another health-led programme that places the relationship at the centre of prevention.

The CHPP is a preventive programme where the focus is on anticipatory guidance, preparing for the future and promoting choices and behaviours that will improve outcomes for children. The aim is to make discussions on relationships a routine part of the CHPP. Practitioners delivering the CHPP do not need to be 'marriage guidance counsellors' but they do need to be psychologically minded and able to discuss relationship issues in families. This is skilled work and I am grateful for the contribution One Plus One has made to the confidence and skill of practitioners, in particular health visitors who have lead responsibility for the CHPP.

Dr Sheila Shribman
National Clinical Director
Children, Young People and Maternity Services
Department of Health, Partnerships for Children, Family and Maternity Division
October 2008

Contents

Introduction

There is now compelling evidence that how parents get on – or don't get on – influences children's lives and child outcomes. Most children still grow up in a home headed by a couple, although for some children the couple with whom they live includes only one of their biological parents. If these children are also in touch with their other biological parent, and most will be, the quality of the parenting they receive will be affected by how all these adults get on with each other. The founding phase of family life – when partners become parents – is a particularly vulnerable time for couples: relationship satisfaction declines and levels of conflict rise. It is also a time when practitioners routinely come into contact with couples.

In One Plus One's work with families we identified the 'turned to moment' – a moment when a parent turns to a practitioner with a relationship issue, often under the guise of a problem with their child. Generally, practitioners working in the frontline with families are not trained to support couple relationships; many have told us this limits the help they can offer families and some admit they find it hard to cope when confronted by couples in conflict.

Over the past two decades One Plus One has been investigating what training and other resources increase the confidence of frontline practitioners to offer effective support to couples and to individuals experiencing distress from a current or former relationship.

In this sourcebook, Jenny Reynolds has brought together the wealth of knowledge and expertise from One Plus One's research and practice development teams, to equip practitioners with sufficient understanding of how relationships work and why they go wrong, and the basic skills to engage with parents at times of change, challenge or crisis in their relationship, in order to offer effective support to couples and their families as part of their routine practice.

Penny Mansfield
Director One Plus One

Publication Outline

This book is in three parts. **Part 1 – Couple Relationships: Why do they matter?** summarises the research evidence that links the couple relationship to children's well-being. This ranges from evidence on the links between infant development and maternal stress, often resulting from problems in the partnership, to the impact of relationship conflict and breakdown on children's immediate and long-term life chances.

The evidence is set in the context of the current policy climate, including workforce reforms and family support initiatives. It maps out:

- the move from a child-centred policy focus, through, for example, *Every Child Matters* (Department for Children, Schools and Families, 2003);

- to the growing emphasis on parenting, exemplified in, for example, *Every Parent Matters* (Department for Education and Skills, 2007); and

- the growing recognition of the impact of the couple relationship on parenting and children's life chances in documents such as the updated *Child Health Promotion Programme* (Department of Health and Department for Children, Schools and Families, 2008) and *The Children's Plan* (Department for Children, Schools and Families, 2007).

Finally, it highlights the framework that One Plus One has developed in order to provide practitioners working with families the tools, time and confidence to engage with the relationship between parents.

Readers are provided with an overview of how relationships work in **Part 2 – Understanding Couple Relationships**. Drawing on a body of international research it explores:

- forming relationships, including what we bring to a relationship;

- how relationships work, including how they change and the role of conflict and support;

- what happens in relationships when couples face significant challenges, such as chronic ill-health, financial pressures, infidelity or sexual difficulties;

- relationship breakdown and what it means for partners and their children; and

- difference and diversity, including the relationships of young parents, those parenting alone, stepfamilies, and gay and lesbian partners.

These strands are brought together in a model that outlines how the experiences and characteristics that each partner brings to a relationship interact with the life events they experience to shape how partners get on. How they relate can set partners on a path towards building their own and their relationship's resilience or entrap them in ways of communicating that undermine the relationship and the love, affection and support that partners provide one another.

Part 3 – Working with Couple Relationships moves the focus onto the practitioner. It highlights key skills for working with the couple relationship. The skills are explored in the context of the Brief encounters® framework – based on One Plus One's training course for family practitioners. The framework is a three stage model of support designed to free practitioners up to listen to a client while managing the, often limited, time available to respond. It covers:

- Stage One – responding to 'the turned to moment' when a problem is raised by the client or observed by the practitioner;

- Stage Two – listening, exploring and understanding what is going on and supporting the client to find their own solutions;
- Stage Three – reviewing progress and ending the 'encounter'.

A case study has been woven through the stages in order to support practitioners in taking the skills and approach into their practice. It is backed up by a series of exercises.

Throughout the book quotes from couples and practitioners illustrate important points and ensure that theory remains grounded in people's daily lives and experiences. The quotes are drawn from the range of research that One Plus One has conducted with the public and family practitioners. Quotes from children have been reproduced from publications exploring children's experiences of separation and divorce.[1] The personal details of those who have been quoted have been changed to protect their anonymity.

Resources

The book ends with helpful resources including:

- information on further training;
- a recommended reading list;
- a series of resources that can be photocopied to use with parents;
- a web-link to a series of video clips that exemplify the Brief encounters® approach.

Many of the skills outlined in Part Three are demonstrated in a series of clips available on One Plus One's website **www.oneplusone.org.uk**. You can also draw on resources that you can use with couples or that they can access themselves on One Plus One's site for couples **www.thecoupleconnection.net**. The site provides interactive information, resources and exercises for individuals and couples. Many of the graphics included in Part Three have been animated and narrated for thecoupleconnection.net and therefore provide readers with an additional means of engaging with new material.

1. Neale, B. and Flowerdew, J. (2004) Parent Problems 2: Looking back on our parents divorce. Young Voice
Neale, B. and Wade, A. (2000) Parent Problems! – Children's views on life when parents split up. Young Voice
Trinder, L., Beek, M and Connolly, J. (2002) How parents and children negotiate and experience contact after divorce. Published for the Joseph Rowntree Foundation by YPS

Part 1: Couple relationships: why do they matter?

"a caring partner, who shares the responsibilities and joys of raising children, and who is there for advice and support when problems arise, is the most potent protective factor a parent can have."

(Professor Mavis Hetherington, 2003)

1. The importance of the couple relationship

After three decades of studying the ups and downs of family life, Professor Hetherington (2003) concludes that good partners help make good parents. Most children seem to know this innately. Seven out of ten teenagers felt that how well parents get on is important to raising happy children (National Family and Parenting Institute, 2000). When things are not going well between parents children start to worry. Twenty eight per cent of calls to ChildLine – a free helpline for children – related to concerns about their parents' relationship, their fears about parents splitting up and worries about being the cause (ChildLine, 1998).

"When rows started I would run up to my room which was at the top of the house. If I shut the door and hummed to myself I couldn't hear them. But then I would stop and if I couldn't hear them I would start worrying that they might have gone and left me."

(Ed, Watford)

If parents cannot resolve their problems, the child's distress often becomes apparent in his or her behavioural, social or emotional development (Reynolds, 2001). If the relationship breaks down, children are likely to continue to feel the effects of their parents' relationship difficulties for up to two years after the separation (Pryor and Rodgers, 2001). For a small minority of children, the effects continue into adulthood.

Many parents are so distracted by their own problems that they do not realise what impact their relationship is having on the children. Or if they do realise, they do not know what to do about it. Those working with families, such as health visitors, family workers, midwives, and GPs, often realise what is happening but feel uncertain about raising the subject or unsure about how to help (Ayles and Reynolds, 2001).

This publication provides those on the frontline with a basic understanding of how relationships work and the tools to use that information to support couples who encounter a difficult patch. No one is better placed to respond to these problems. Family practitioners are a trusted feature of family life. They are often turned to first when couples do not know where else to go (Brannen and Collard, 1982; Corney, 1990; Ayles and Reynolds, 2001). Many practitioners are already using their listening skills and knowledge of family development to ease couples through difficult patches. This includes those who have taken One Plus One's Brief encounters® training, which gives participants a framework for supporting parents

---

Box 1.1: Children and parental conflict

Children who are exposed to embittered, antagonistic conflict or silent hostility between parents are more likely to develop either:

- behavioural problems apparent in acting up, aggression and anger;
- emotional problems that manifest themselves as depressed, withdrawn behaviour;
- social and educational problems that make it hard to get on with others and difficult to succeed at school.

when they face relationship difficulties. Over 3,500 practitioners have been trained since the course was launched in 1993. As many of these practitioners would say themselves, support is not about counselling. It is about giving parents enough time and understanding to help them work out their own solutions. And it is about making sure practitioners have a model for providing that help in the context of their busy caseloads and personal concerns.

"I know that I will listen more carefully in case there is an underlying problem that is hard for the parents to just 'blurt' out and I feel better equipped to listen and help them to help themselves."

(Home-Start worker)

Parents invariably welcome the support that they have received. Here is one parent who confided in her community mother when things were difficult:

Interviewer: *"How did that help, how did the listening help?"*

Mother: *"Because it took, because it felt like I'd poured everything out of me and it had all gone into her, and she'd heard every word..."*

(Tanya, Stockport)

Couple relationships and family policy

Family policy is beginning to take on board the significant role that the couple relationship plays in helping children to realise their full potential. Following the launch of *Every Child Matters* (Department for Education and Skills, 2003) the policy focus for some years was on children first, parents second. (See Appendix 1 for a detailed family policy timeline).

Table 1.1: The role of the couple relationship in family policy

1998	**Supporting Families** – Consultation paper setting out Labour's vision for families.
2003	**Every Child Matters** – Green Paper proposing a range of initiatives to improve support for children and parents and enhance joined up working, e.g. Children's Trusts, Common Assessment Framework.
2004	**National Service Framework for Children, Young People and Maternity Services** – DoH guidance on a child-centred approach with a particular emphasis on supporting parents.
2004	**The Children's Act** – the legal underpinning for Every Child Matters.
2005	**Support for Parents; The Best Start for Children** – reaffirming the Government's commitment to optimising outcomes for children through support for parents.
2007	**Making it Better: For Mother and Baby** – new vision for maternity services.
2007	**Every Parent Matters** – first document clearly setting out policies relating specifically to parenting.
2007	**Aiming High: Supporting Families** – Treasury report of services for children and young people that also reiterates the Government's commitment to supporting parental relationships.
2007	**Children's Plan** – setting out the Government's vision for children over the next 10 years.
2008	**Think Family: Improving the life chances of families at risk** – highlighting the need for joined up work between adults' and children's services around the needs of the family.
2008	**Child Health Promotion Programme** – the early intervention and prevention public health programme that is integral to universal services for children and families.

More recently, policy has begun to realise that supporting children means supporting their parents both in their parenting and in their relationships. Take the *Children's Plan*, which sets out the Government's vision for the next 10 years:

"An effective family policy must start with supporting strong couple relationships and stable, positive relationships within families."

(Department for Children, Schools and Families, 2007)

or *Aiming High: Supporting Families:*

"Children's outcomes are best when they grow up in a stable family structure with a positive relationship between parents. The quality of each parent's relationship with the other is vital."

(HM Treasury, 2007, p.29 2.54)

This is not to say that a married couple with 2.5 children is the only setting in which children will thrive. It is a recognition that how parents get on together affects how their children get on in life. Getting on together might happen in all sorts of ways – living together, living apart, sharing parenting with a new partner – but it needs to happen if children are to thrive. The encouragement to *'Think Family'* (Cabinet Office, 2008) sums up this shift in policy and practice.

Box 1.2: Family Policy and support for couples

Aiming High: Supporting Families (HM Treasury, 2007)
"Children's outcomes are best when they grow up in a stable family structure with a positive relationship between parents… The quality of each parent's relationship with the other is vital. Government wants to support stable relationships between parents. However, where relationships break down, the Government also wants to provide the necessary support to ensure children get the best start."

Building on Progress: Families – Policy Review (Cabinet Office, May 2007)
"Specifically, there are three areas of family policy where the state should act. First, it should address those things that damage families and impair the life chances of the children within them, such as poverty, low aspirations, poor parenting and conflict in relationships."

Children's Plan: Building Brighter Futures (DCSF, 2007)
"An effective family policy must start with supporting strong couple relationships and stable, positive relationships within families. Good local services are important in helping families cope with the inevitable stresses and strains, in meeting their needs and giving them the opportunity to achieve a good quality of life. In addition, there are times in the normal course of events for every family when the demands on parents can be especially acute and lead to tension in their relationship. It is important that services can recognise and support people through those periods of instability."

Think Family: Improving the Life Chances of Children at Risk (Cabinet Office, 2008)
"Addressing parental problems is key to achieving positive outcomes for the wider family and adults' services are more likely to engage parents if they are sensitive to their family circumstances. Services that adapt to fit the family can often offer more appropriate and effective support."

Future directions

Although the focus on parental support has emerged out of the policies of a Labour led government, Tory party proposals are even more explicit in their focus on the couple relationship, (see *Breakthrough Britain: the Next Generation,* Centre for Social Justice, 2008). The Conservatives are also keen to ensure that parents under pressure receive support early, before couples reach a crisis. This means that the importance of relationships is seen across parties as a key feature of family support. Both parties have emphasised the need to strengthen relationships, provide early intervention and better support to parents when they are separating.

The impact of the couple relationship

A large-scale review found that 'poor relationships in the home', including those between parents and between parents and their children, have an impact on the future physical and mental health of children, even after taking account of their socio-economic status (Stewart-Brown and Shaw, 2004). The association between the parents' relationship and outcomes for the family is so strong that it has been described by one researcher as the 'conductor of the family orchestra' (Harold, 2001). It shapes the influence of other family factors on children's well-being.

Researchers have mapped out the impact of the couple relationship on children's well-being from the antenatal period through to adulthood. The relationship:

- influences maternal stress in the perinatal period. Maternal stress, in turn, has been associated with the development of children's emotional or cognitive problems, including attention deficit disorder and hyperactivity, anxiety and language delay. The findings are separate from any impact associated with the mother's depressed or anxious state after the birth (see Box 1.3);

- affects the male partner's hormonal readiness to become a nurturing father (see Box 1.4);

- influences parents' capacity to parent (see Box 1.4);

- shapes fathers' involvement with their children (see Box 1.4); and

- promotes partners' physical and mental health when it is working well and undermines it when things are going wrong (see McAllister, 1995; Coleman and Glenn, forthcoming).

Because children often lack the capacity or opportunity to process the disturbing feelings and fears they experience when their parents are at odds, they express them through their behaviour, moods, and relationships (Harold et al., 2007). This leaves them vulnerable to: emotional and behavioural problems; difficulties establishing good relationships with others; and a failure to reach their educational potential.

"I was an only child so when my parents were not getting on it was desperate. They didn't have big fights just incessant squabbling. I remember feeling that I had to get them to stop and give me attention. If we were out, running off was a good way to get them to start noticing that I was there."

(Annie, Worthing)

The evidence that lays out these relationships is summarised in the review boxes on the following pages.

Figure 1.1: Children and parental conflict[2]

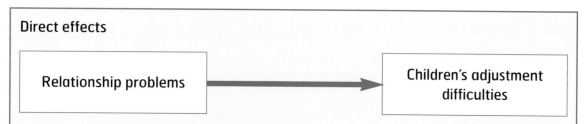

Direct effects

| Relationship problems | → | Children's adjustment difficulties |

Children look and learn: Conflict can have a direct impact on children's adjustment because children copy their parents' behaviour – aggression, contempt, hostility, sulking, and withdrawing - the usual features of couple conflict. Children may also attempt to distract parents by misbehaving when parents quarrel. If the child succeeds in ending the fight, she may 'act up' again and again. Consequently, bad behaviour is rewarded by the ending of the quarrel.

The stress of warring parents: Exposure to parental conflict is also stressful for children, whatever their age. Even children as young as one and two years old have been found to become distressed when adults argue.

Expecting the worst: Children develop expectations about parental conflict based on past experiences. Children whose parents work out their differences are less likely to worry about the repercussions for themselves. However, children whose parents find it difficult to manage conflict become more disturbed even when their parents have minor disputes. Children can carry these expectations into other situations. Children then become troubled when caught up in disagreements with peers, siblings and other adults.

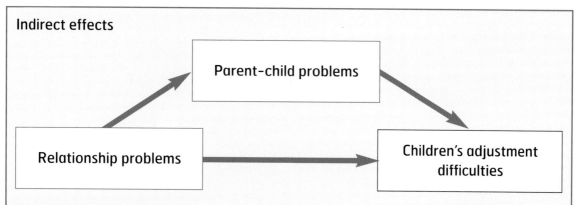

Indirect effects

Distressed and distracted parents
Unhappy parents are likely to be less emotionally available to their children and more inconsistent in how they discipline a child from day to day. Distressed parents are also more likely to disagree with each other about parenting. This can result in one parent building an alliance with the child against the other parent which undermines the child's relationship with the other parent and leaves the child vulnerable to rejection if parents are reconciled.

continued...

2. This section is based on the findings of a review of international studies on the impact of parental conflict on children (Reynolds, 2001).

Figure 1.1 continued...

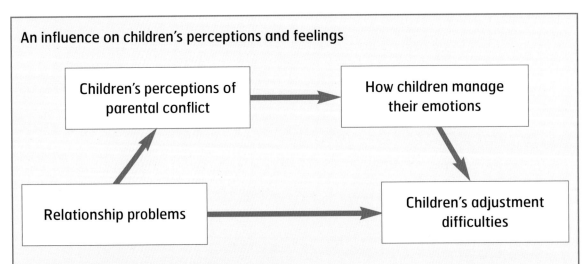

An influence on children's perceptions and feelings

Children's perceptions of parental conflict → How children manage their emotions

Relationship problems → Children's perceptions of parental conflict

How children manage their emotions → Children's adjustment difficulties

Relationship problems → Children's adjustment difficulties

Children try to make sense of their parents' conflict

How children make sense of parental conflict and the meanings they attribute to it are an important factor in how discord affects their well-being. For example, conflict may be harmful if children believe they are to blame for their parents' difficulties (Harold et al., 2007). Which means that when parents argue again the child will be anxious about how it will affect them, for example, 'will their parents turn their anger on the child and blame them for the relationship problems?'

Children's emotional security is undermined by parental fighting

Children's perceptions of parental conflict can threaten their emotional security, undermine their confidence in the relationship with their parents, and make them question whether the family will stay together. This is especially true of children who have been exposed to parental conflict over a long period of time.

Box 1.3 summarises the evidence on the impact of stress during pregnancy and the implications for childhood development. Maternal stress has been linked to a range of negative emotional and behavioural outcomes. Problems in the couple relationship are a frequent source of stress.

Box 1.3: Maternal stress and infant development

Implications

Although it is difficult to establish causal links in such complex processes, research has found an association between stress arising from relationship problems in the antenatal period and poorer infant cognition and higher fearfulness (Bergman et al., 2007). In addition, children of mothers going through a separation or divorce during pregnancy, or who had experienced 'cruelty by the partner', are more likely to display lower scores on measures of cognitive development (Bergman et al., 2007).

Stress and anxiety are very common in late pregnancy – more so than in the postpartum period (Heron et al., 2004). Its prevalence means that up to 15 per cent of behavioural and emotional problems could be explained by antenatal stress.

Outcomes

Neonatal outcomes

- Maternal stress, ranging from daily hassles to depression and anxiety, is associated with an increased risk of slower growth and smaller babies for gestational age and an increased risk of pre-term and earlier delivery. These, in turn, are risk factors for impaired cognitive and social developmental outcomes (Wadhwa, 2005; Wadhwa et al., 2001).

Infant and childhood outcomes

- Antenatal depression and anxiety have been linked to infant behavioural patterns indicative of shyness and anxiety disorders in later childhood (Kagan et al., 1987).

- Researchers have also found a link between antenatal stress and attention deficit hyperactivity disorder (ADHD) in four to 15 year olds (O'Connor et al., 2002; Van den Bergh et al., 2005)

- Women in the top 15 per cent of symptoms for anxiety at 32 weeks gestation had double the risk (increased from 5 per cent to ten per cent) of having children with behavioural problems at four and seven years of age, even after taking account of other factors (O'Connor et al., 2002).

Adult outcomes

- Studies also demonstrate an association between maternal exposure to traumatic events and psychopathology in adulthood (Talge et al., 2007).

Processes

Researchers are still working on understanding how stress affects neurodevelopment. There appear to be points during the development of the brain, such as at 18 weeks and 32 weeks, when it is particularly sensitive to the impact of stress (O'Connor et al., 2002, 2003). It is also difficult to establish causality. Women who are prone to stress and anxiety are also more vulnerable to relationship difficulties and more likely to find pregnancy stressful.

Box 1.4: Couple relationships and parenting

Belsky (1984) calls the couple relationship "the principal support system for parents".

- Parents in a happy relationship interact more positively with their infant, preschool child, and school age child (Simons et al., 1993; Levy-Schiff, 1994; Lindahl et al., 1997; Carlson and McLanahan, 2005).

- A well functioning couple relationship is associated with sensitive, warm and accepting parenting (Grych, 2002).

- A poorer relationship is linked to permissive parenting and more negative parent-child relationships (Easterbrooks and Emde, 1988; DeVito and Hopkins, 2001).

- These parenting behaviours are associated with poorer outcomes for children.

Relationship intimacy in pregnancy and fathers' hormonal readiness for parenting

- Men experience hormonal changes during the antenatal period, such as a reduction in testosterone, which encourage them to bond with the infant. These changes are triggered during the pregnancy as their partner's hormonal levels change in the run up to the delivery. Being involved with a partner during pregnancy is therefore an important precursor to being a prepared and involved father (Storey et al. 2000).

More important to fathers than mothers

- The couple relationship has a greater impact on the father's relationship with his children (e.g. Cummings and O'Reilly, 1997) than on the mother's (e.g. Carlson and McLanahan, 2005; Pike et al., 2006).

- Researchers have found links between parental conflict and fathers' parenting control, acceptance, harsh discipline and the overall quality of their parenting (Krishnakumar and Buehler, 2000).

- In general, men are more likely to see being a father and a husband as a 'package deal', with one role dependent on the other (Allen and Daly, 2004). If there are problems in the relationship fathers have a much more difficult time being involved with their children, which weakens the father-child relationship (Coiro and Emery, 1998).

Mothers – enablers or gatekeepers?

Mothers are important enablers. When mothers are supportive of their partner's parenting, for example, they see them as competent and believe parenting is a joint venture, men are more likely to be:

- involved with, and responsible for, their children (Doherty et al., 1998);

- feel recognised as a parental figure (Jordan, 1990);

- place a greater importance on their father role identity (Paisley et al., 2002);

- and feel more satisfaction, pleasure, competence, and comfort in their paternal role (see Allen and Daly, 2004).

Fathers: an important source of support and stability

Although fathering is more vulnerable to relationship difficulties, fathers are also important enablers.

- The amount of support a mother receives from her partner has been linked to her care-giving competence and the quality of attachment between mother and child (Fincham and Hall, 2005).

- When fathers are emotionally supportive their partners are more likely to enjoy a greater sense of well being, good postpartum mental health (Gjerdingen et al., 1991), and have a relatively problem free pregnancy, delivery process, and nursing experience (Biller, 1993).

- Relationships where the father is 'hands-on' are more stable. This appears to be partly because women whose partners are involved in parenting are happier in the relationship than those with more hands-off partners (Kalmijn, 1999).

Box 1.5: Relationship breakdown and children

Impact

Overall, children from separated families have between 1.5 to twice the risk of an adverse outcome compared to children from intact families. This risk is not large. However, the differences are significant when they are seen in the context of population well-being. Assuming that 25% of children experience parental separation, it means that 20% of social, emotional and behavioural problems in the population are due to the increased risks associated with separation and divorce (Pryor and Rodgers, 2001).

Outcomes

A large-scale review of the impact of relationship breakdown (Pryor and Rodgers, 2001) concludes that:

- Differences in outcomes for children are apparent across a range of areas, including social, psychological and physical development.

- The effects persist into adulthood and through it. For example, differences in alcohol use are greater in later adulthood.

- The impact is greatest on how children from divorced or separated homes manage family and intimate relationships in adolescence and adulthood. Again, the impact is lasting and more pertinent in adulthood than childhood.

- These lasting effects point to the so-called 'intergenerational transmission' of poor relationship management skills and vulnerability to divorce.

- Some children, however, benefit when parents with very troubled relationships finally go their separate ways.

Processes

Poorer outcomes for children from divorced and separated homes are explained by a complex interplay between factors that are there before, during and after the separation. Two important factors are the children's experience of parental conflict before, during and after the separation (see Part 2) and the impact of relationship difficulties on parenting (see Box 1.3). When children go through a series of family transitions, i.e. the breakdown of a subsequent parental relationship and setting up of another new family, they tend to do worse.

From Every Child Matters to the Child Health Promotion Programme

Where does this evidence leave family health practitioners and others working on the frontline with families? The *Child Health Promotion Programme* (CHPP) (Department of Health and Department for Children, Schools and Families, 2008) acknowledges the importance of taking account of the couple relationship. For example, it encourages practitioners to recognise and respond to unstable or troubled relationships as a risk factor for poor child outcomes during pregnancy (p.15). The couple relationship is identified as a topic that might be addressed during a health and development review (p.18). The CHPP also reiterates the beneficial impact on children's development of an involved father. As Box 1.4 highlights, fathers are much more likely to be involved if they are in a supportive relationship with the mother.

The updated CHPP also requires practitioners to consider new evidence on the impact of positive parenting and parent-child relationships on children's well-being. Some of the evidence is touched on in this publication, such as the relationship between maternal stress and foetal development. But more importantly, this publication puts the evidence in a broader context by explaining its relevance to the couple relationship. The links between the core requirements of the CHPP and our understanding of the link between couple relationships are mapped out in Box 1.6.

Box 1.6 : The couple relationship and the Child Health Promotion Programme

The core requirements of the CHPP		Why supporting the couple relationship meets those requirements
• recognise and respond to factors that place families at risk of poor outcomes and how those factors can combine together to create a multiplying effect		• problems in the couple relationship have been linked to poor parental mental health, such as depression and alcohol abuse, and are crucial to understanding the context in which children are growing up and the factors that may jeopardise their well-being (McAllister, 1995).
• recognise and address mental health problems in parents		• parental depression and family stresses, such as socio-economic pressure and work stress, increase the likelihood of discord as well as further reduce parents' ability to engage positively with each other and with their children. If parents get on well under pressure they can reduce the risk of harm to the child and provide helpful models of coping (see Part 2).
• recognise and encourage the factors that promote family resilience and well-being		• a well-functioning relationship acts as a buffer against the stresses and strains of parenting and is a significant source of support for the other parent (Quinton, 1999; Hetherington, 2003).
• promote the social and emotional development of infants and young children		• problems in the couple relationship can affect an infant's ability to form a secure attachment to his or her primary carer(s) (Reynolds, 2001).
• take account of the parenting and family context when assessing an infant's health and development		• problems in the couple relationship have also been linked to children's adjustment difficulties (Reynolds, 2001).
• support parenting		• a poorly functioning relationship can impair parenting (Reynolds, 2001).

The requirements of the CHPP should also be considered in the broader context of the standards in the *National Service Framework for Children, Young People and Maternity Services* (Department of Health and Department for Education and Skills, 2004) that it updates and extends. These standards are also a means of meeting some of the Public Service Agreements that extend across Government (see p.64 CHPP). Again, the evidence is strong for why supporting the couple relationship is an important tool in delivering these standards (see Box 1.7).

As the evidence summarised in this chapter demonstrates, supporting parenting as part of the CHPP also means supporting the couple relationship. Family practitioners' unique access to parents during this time puts them in a strong position to do this. It has been described as a 'magic moment' (Parke, 2004). As a time of challenge and change, parents are motivated and open to making positive changes in their behaviour. For example, a recent study offered psychoeducational, skills-based classes delivered within the framework of hospital antenatal classes (Feinberg and Kan, 2008). The programme had a beneficial impact on coparental support, maternal depression and anxiety, problems in the parent-child relationship and several indicators of infant regulation. A minimum amount of help, particularly if it is offered early, can have maximum impact because the family system is already in a process of change in response to the stresses it is experiencing (Caplan, 1964; Rappoport, 1977). Fathers are usually involved and partners, regardless of marital status, have high expectations for the future (Lawrence et al., 2008).

Box 1.7: Public Service Agreements and supporting couples – the evidence

PSA 12 – Improve the health and wellbeing of children and young people
Children's physical, emotional and behavioural wellbeing are at risk when they are exposed to embittered, unresolved conflict between their parents (Harold, 2001).

PSA 10 – Raise the educational achievement of all children and young people
Children do worse at school, educationally and socially, when parents cannot get on (Reynolds, 2001).

PSA 18 – Promote better health for all
Parents' and children's health are affected by good relationships in the home (McAllister 1995; Stewart-Brown and Shaw, 2004)

PSA 14 – Increase the number of children and young people on the path to success
Children who enjoy the benefits of a stable and happy home are more likely to achieve their potential into adulthood. Children who experience the break down of the family are at greater risk of problems in their own relationships and challenges to their wellbeing in adulthood (Pryor and Rodgers, 2001).

Box 1.8: Parenting interventions and supporting couples

An important feature of the new CHPP, building on National Service Framework Standard 2 'Promoting Parenting', is the support it seeks to provide parents. Research demonstrates that where there are problems between parents, parenting support is more effective if it addresses those difficulties. This was apparent in a study that compared the impact of a child management training programme (CMT) and a combination of CMT and partner support training (focused on issues such as conflict and communication) (Dadds et al., 1987). When the outcomes for children of discordant parents were compared, children whose parents received the combined treatment performed better than children whose parents participated in the CMT only.

"Often when parents come on courses they say it is about the young person's behaviour, and you kind of get that feeling that there is something else going on here. Then at the third or fourth session you realise that the issue is actually between the parents, not between the parents and the young person."

(Parenting Course Facilitator)

In a separate study, couples whose children were starting school took part in either couple focused groups, parenting focused groups or a control group (Cowan et al., 2005). As expected, the groups had an impact on couple relationships and parenting respectively and these outcomes were associated with child adjustment one to two years later. However, couples in the parenting focused groups showed improvements in parenting but not marital interaction, whereas couples in the relationship focused groups improved in both areas.

One Plus One has developed a training package for parent educators – *My Mum and Dad Argue a Lot* (Morrod and Munro, 2006) – that provides them with the information, skills and resources they need to address couple conflict issues. The resources that accompany it mean that participants can bolt the module onto existing parenting courses. The training was developed because of a lack of manual based resources for working with couple conflict in the context of parent education and support.

A changing workforce

Policy is also beginning to recognise that how practitioners work with families – the respect, attention and understanding they demonstrate – are some of the most powerful tools they have in supporting healthy and happy family development. Workforce developments, such as the consultation and publication around nursing, *Modernising Nursing Careers* (2006), the *Review of the Role of Health Visitors* (2007) and the introduction of the *Common Core of Skills and Knowledge for the Children's Workforce* (2005) have run alongside the expanding family policy agenda (see Policy Timeline, Appendix 1). These have sought to ensure

the workforce has the appropriate skills and necessary structures to deliver effective, whole-family support. Developments were set in motion by the *Every Child Matter's* (2003) agenda and the strategies it proposed to deliver the five children's outcomes. They have resulted in:

- an expansion and diversification of the workforce involved in supporting children and parents;

- a changed role for health visitors as they take responsibility for mixed-skills teams in delivering the CHPP;

- the delivery of support from new and diverse settings, such as Children's Centres and Extended Schools; and
- a new emphasis on the skills required to work with children and parents.

The skills for working with families

The CHPP, that brings together many of these changes, places great emphasis on appropriate skills for working with parents. Skilled practitioners, from a range of backgrounds, are expected to be able to form a partnership with the parents and use purposeful listening and guiding questions in order to set a shared agenda that meets the needs of the parent and enables the practitioner to deliver the CHPP (p.19).

The tools for working with the couple relationship outlined in this publication are foundational to this way of working. They offer models of good practice in:
- building and managing relationships with parents;
- developing sensitive listening skills; and
- being parent led.

The tools also recognise the pressures under which practitioners work – a lack of time, a pressing caseload, and sometimes, feeling ill-equipped to respond to the range of needs and issues with which they are faced.

"We've got too much to do and the thing is, you see, if you open something up, have you got the time to devote to it?"

(District Nurse)

The Brief encounters® model – based on One Plus One's training course – provides a framework to respond to parents' needs and to set the boundaries around what the practitioner is able to offer. It outlines the stages of a supportive encounter with a client and some of the essential skills and knowledge that will guide a practitioner through that encounter.

Figure 1.2: The Stages of a Brief Encounter

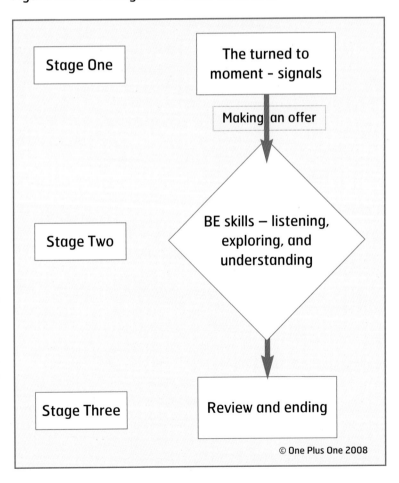

Stage One — The turned to moment - signals

Making an offer

Stage Two — BE skills – listening, exploring, and understanding

Stage Three — Review and ending

© One Plus One 2008

The value of this training has been recognised in recent Government publications, including: *Sure Start Children's Centres Practice Guidance* (Department of Health and Department for Education and Skills, 2005), the *Children's Plan* (Department for Children, Schools and Families, 2007), *Think Family* (Cabinet Office, 2008) and the CHPP (Department of Health and Department for Children, Schools and Families, 2008). It also dovetails with some of the other recommended approaches, such as motivational interviewing.

The Children's Plan: Building Brighter Futures (2007)

"Health visitors through the One Plus One programme are being trained to learn to listen to parents, spot problems between them following the birth of a baby, and offer specific help to the couple as well as ensuring the healthy development of the child."

Sure Start Children's Centres: Practice Guidance (2005)

"Home visiting can also be a good opportunity to engage with both parents together, but visitors will need the skill and confidence to negotiate the relationship between the adult couple. Training such as Brief encounters® from One Plus One (www.oneplusone.org.uk) has been shown to be very effective for such practitioners."

Think Family: Improving outcomes for families at risk (2008)

"One Plus One trains practitioners, including those in health, education, social care and legal services, to deal with relationship conflict and to help build strong family relationships."

Child Health Promotion Programme (2008)

"Techniques to promote a trusting relationship and develop problem-solving abilities within the family e.g. promotional / motivational interviewing; Family Partnership Model; the Solihull approach; and One Plus One's Brief encounters® should be used."

The Conservative party have also drawn attention to the value of the Brief encounters® approach. It is highlighted in their report on family policy, *Breakthrough Britain: the Next Generation* (Centre for Social Justice, 2008). This also sets out their vision for increasing the presence of health visitors in the lives of young families and maintaining a strong, universal service.

How Brief encounters® helps

Practitioners who have been trained in the Brief encounters® approach talk about feeling more confident, knowledgeable and skilled in addressing problems between parents.

"Since the course I have found when I visit families to assess the need I am a lot more confident in my approach when talking about relationships. I have more understanding. A mum said 'I feel better already' and could I come back for another chat!"

(Home-Start worker)

The majority of health visitors interviewed as part of a randomised controlled trial of screening for relationship difficulties amongst new mothers and training for health visitors thought that their interventions had often had a positive impact on the couple relationship and that it had helped mothers get through a difficult time (Simons et al., 2003). Mothers who took part in the trial talked about the importance of having someone to whom they could unburden themselves: of 'just being able to talk to someone'; of her 'just being there – there was no-one else for me to talk to'; of 'getting something off my chest I couldn't say to anyone else'.

They also talked about the practical help that they received. One said the health visitor made her realise she should talk to her partner about the effect an aspect of his behaviour was having on their relationship. Another said that without the health visitor's intervention 'He'd have still been assaulting me'.

An independent evaluation conducted by the University of Greenwich (Corney, 1998) found that 'the Brief encounters® training has been a remarkable success'. Six months after training:

- 94 per cent of practitioners trained were using the model, with over half using it daily or weekly;

- 91 per cent were more able to manage their involvement in their clients' problems; and

- 88 per cent learned to manage their time more effectively.

More recently, Community Mothers, Home Start volunteers, Health Visitors, and Parent Educators who have been involved in One Plus One training programmes have described improvements in their confidence, skills, knowledge, and readiness to discuss problems between parents (Reynolds, 2002; Reynolds et al., 2002; Ayles, 2003; Corney et al., 2006).

More information about training in Brief encounters® as well as other sources of training, information and support are provided in Appendix 2.

Key Messages

- The couple relationship has a huge impact on children's well-being. When things are going wrong between parents their children are at greater risk of emotional, social and behavioural difficulties.

- Support for families has begun to recognise this important link. The CHPP encourages practitioners to support parents who are struggling with their relationships at crucial times of change or challenge.

- The Brief encounter® tools for supporting couples build on practitioners' existing skill base of attentive listening and enabling support. They also include a framework that helps practitioners to provide support within the context of the personal and professional resources at their disposal.

Part 2: Understanding Couple Relationships

"... the distinguishing feature of these (enduring) relationships is the sense and primacy of 'coupleness'... both partners have the goodwill necessary to learn and engage in the behaviours that keep alive the emotional connection that brought them together in the first place."

(Robyn Parker, 2002)

An introduction to couple relationships

Relationships are complex. They are organic and changing. Sometimes they are the source of great anguish and at other times a safe haven and place of comfort and intimacy.

As quotes from newlyweds demonstrate, when they are working well relationships provide:

Belonging	*"The closeness we have makes me feel secure"*
Reassurance	*"He makes me feel good about who I am"*
Guidance	*"I always go first to Pete when I have a problem"*
Reliability	*"She's always there for me"*
Togetherness	*"We're best mates, we have similar interests and aims in life"*
Nurturance	*"Caring for him makes me feel good"*

Although relationships vary enormously and feel deeply personal, researchers have identified patterns of relating that differentiate relationships that are working well from those that are in trouble. The following sections provide:

- key theories and evidence about relationships;
- insight into the challenges relationships face when couples go through difficult times;.
- information about when things go wrong; and
- an understanding of difference and diversity in relationships.

An overview of relationships

Most couples start out 'in love', wanting and hoping for the best for the relationship. However, making a go of it – achieving a loving, stable relationship - is a challenge. It means moving from the heady romantic days to the reality of trying to live together. This was Sharon's experience:

"We were very close... but as we moved on he started to erupt back again ... if I said something he erupted... if I wanted to raise something again it would be a 'not this again'..."

(Sharon, Blackburn)

Managing the journey from romance to reality involves coping with the way in which the relationship changes over time. Over this time couples gradually reassert their independence following the closeness of the early days. How well couples fare depends on their genetic makeup and the personal traits and experiences they bring to a relationship, the life events they encounter on the way and how they communicate and cope during difficult times. Figure 2.2 illustrates how these factors connect.

Figure 2.1: Romance to reality

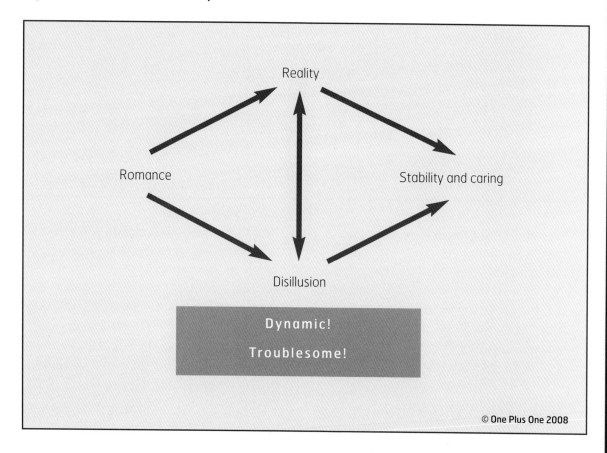

© One Plus One 2008

Figure 2.2: Factors that shape the success of a relationship

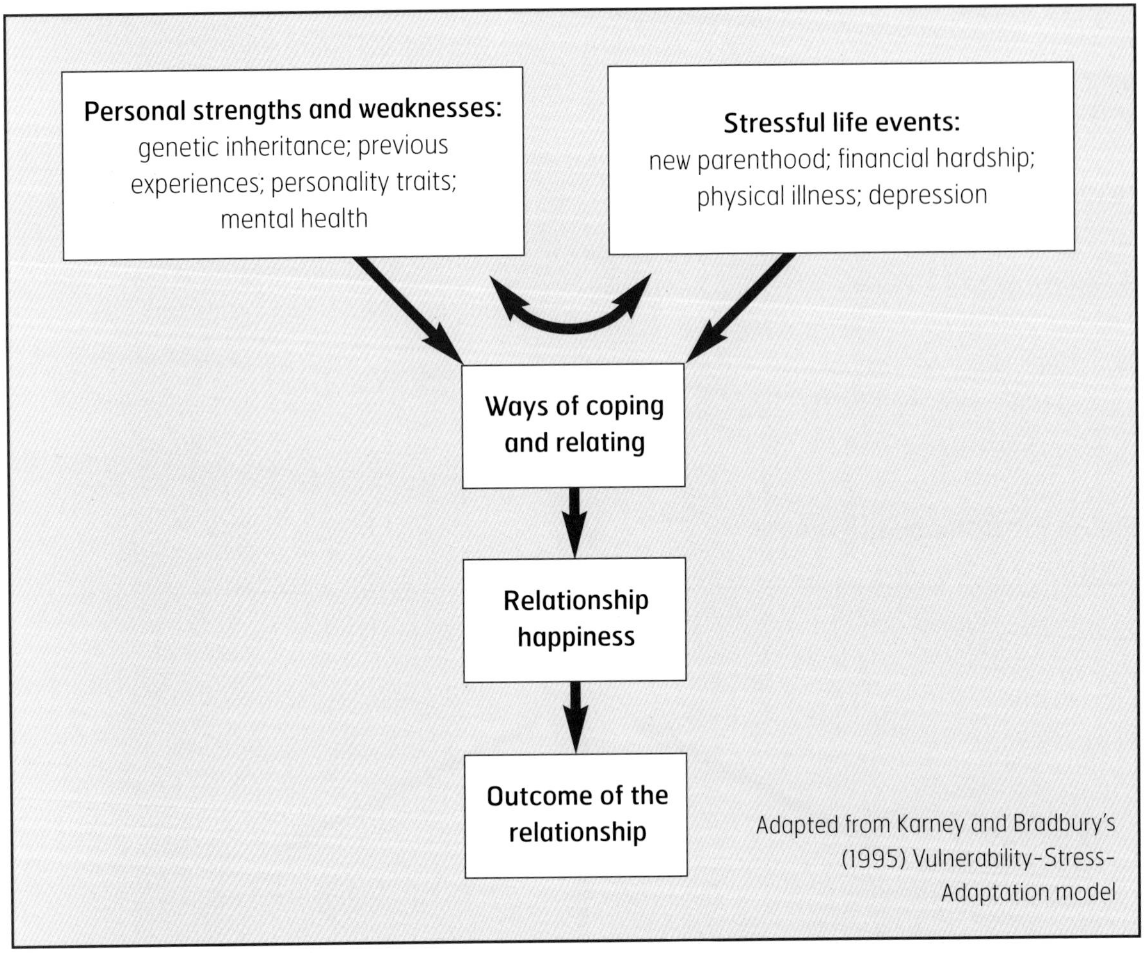

Personal strengths and weaknesses:
genetic inheritance; previous experiences; personality traits; mental health

Stressful life events:
new parenthood; financial hardship; physical illness; depression

Ways of coping and relating

Relationship happiness

Outcome of the relationship

Adapted from Karney and Bradbury's (1995) Vulnerability-Stress-Adaptation model

- **Personal strengths and weaknesses** are sometimes referred to as 'enduring vulnerabilities'. They are the characteristics that each partner brings to the relationship. These include past experiences, their personalities and genetic make-up; beliefs and attitudes about relationships, their family of origin and social background.

- **Ways of coping and relating** – the couple's adaptive processes – sums up how partners relate to one another. It covers: how partners deal with conflict; communicate; support each other; and think about the relationship, their partner and their partner's behaviour.

- **Stressful life events** are the incidents, transitions, or circumstances that put pressure on the couple relationship and create tension or stress.

The model summarises how these factors interact to influence the outcome of a relationship. Partners' personal strengths and weaknesses influence how they relate to one another. They also shape the capacity to cope with the life events that a couple encounter. Couples with relatively poor coping and communication skills might remain happy in the relationship if they do not have to cope with many stressful life events. On the other hand, couples who have to cope with a series of stressful events can run into difficulties even if they bring few enduring vulnerabilities and have developed helpful ways of relating and coping. Some couples know this instinctively! This was Ron's thinking:

"For me it's obvious that if things are rosy, a relationship is rosy, and if things don't go very well, health wise or work wise or whatever, then something's going to suffer. And so if you get a combination of these things not working together you're going to have a rocky ride and you will survive the ride if basically you've got something good together. Then you're okay."

(Ron, Macclesfield)

Ultimately, if couples continue to experience problems getting on these difficulties will eventually undermine the relationship and the couple may eventually separate. If partners adapt successfully to the pressures they face they will strengthen or maintain their relationship and reduce the chances of relationship breakdown. The following sections explore some of these different processes in more detail.

1. What we bring to our relationships

Choosing a partner

The things that attract people to one another and how those traits influence the relationship provide useful insight into how relationships work. For example, past experiences, life events, and previous relationships all affect a person's sense of themselves, their expectations of a relationship and how they relate to a partner. We see this in individuals whose parents divorced. Where one or both partners' parents divorced the relationship is more likely to break down. Why? Individuals learn how to relate to others from watching their parents. They also inherit traits from their parents that can affect how they relate to others (Beach et al., 2004).

"Well, because my dad left when I was young I do think trust is a very, very big part of a relationship, because you know, when I was eight your dad's the first person you learn to trust as a man, isn't he, and you know, he left me and my brother, so you know, my trust in men was not very good. I think that's why I used to not treat blokes very nicely when I was younger, you know."

(Leah, Nottingham)

Partners also bring their inner conflicts, many of which are unconscious or hidden. This is the case with Jo, whose partner is aware of issues she has carried into the partnership as a result of her relationship with her father:

"Jo is a really strong and sometimes dogmatic type of person. On the outside she is not really a person to be trifled with — she doesn't suffer foolish men gladly. She had a huge thing with her father in the past and she is still a little bit testy about that. Sometimes she takes that stuff out on me and sometimes on her brother. I still think she does that sometimes."

(Garry, London)

One theory is that individuals unconsciously choose a partner with whom they can complete the 'unfinished business' of their childhood experiences. This means finding a partner who helps them to engage with some of the hidden parts of themselves as opposed to the 'public self' or the self we show to others. A partner might restore someone's faith in intimacy and closeness after damaging experiences during childhood. A partner might help an individual to feel safe in the world and so help them to manage their overwhelming feelings, such as anxiety and fear. In some cases, one partner is attracted to someone with whom they replay some of the damaging negative relationship experiences of their childhood. For example, a woman whose childhood was marked by domestic violence may go on to choose a partner who turns out to be abusive. Eventually, she may leave him and go on to repair some of these damaging childhood experiences. Some of these processes are depicted in Figure 2.3. The figure is a reminder that a partnership is more than the sum of the two individuals in it. The partnership is a complex system (see Lyons, 1992; Clulow, 2001b).

> **Key point:**
> - Who we choose as a partner and how we interact with them is shaped, in part, by our childhood experiences.

Figure 2.3: Finding a partner – meeting a hidden self

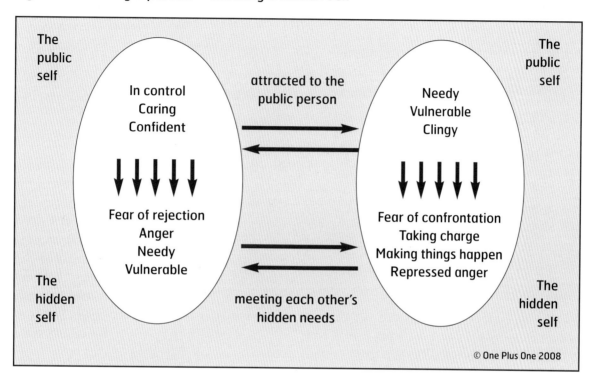

© One Plus One 2008

Choosing a set of problems

Some couples encounter difficulties because the characteristics that initially attracted them to one another subsequently drive them apart. For example, an unassertive woman with low self-esteem might find a dominant partner loving and caring at the outset. But his behaviour will probably become suffocating as time goes on. Similarly, an outgoing and lively woman may bring fun into the life of an introverted partner but could become a source of envy and annoyance after she has enjoyed years in the limelight. In the words of one therapist, when you choose a partner, you choose "a particular set of unsolvable problems that you'll be grappling with for the next ten, twenty, fifty years." (p.13). Choosing a different partner brings the challenges of a different set of problems (Wile, 1988) – see Box 2.1.

Box 2.1. Choosing a set of problems

Paul married Alice who gets loud at parties, which Paul hates. But if Paul had married Susan they would have had a row before the party because Paul is always late and Susan hates to be kept waiting. She would have felt taken for granted, something she is very sensitive about. Paul would have seen her complaining as an attempt to dominate him. Something that he is very sensitive about ... But if Susan had married Nathan ...

(Wile, 1988)

Early experiences of relationships

Adult relationships and attachment

One of the key things that partners bring to a relationship is their attachment style. Attachment theory presupposes that humans have a basic drive to form and sustain relationships, or attachments. Bowlby, the originator of attachment theory, identified certain patterns of behaviour in relationships that are apparent not only among infants and young children, but also in adolescents and adults. Attachment theory is therefore a useful tool for helping to make sense of relationships (e.g. see Clulow, 2001a).

Infant attachments

Attachment theory argues that parents provide a 'secure base' for children from which a child can develop and explore the world and to which the child returns when hurt, threatened, ill or tired. Parents provide a secure base when they are available, responsive, supportive and consistent. This means that they are sensitive to the child's needs and able to nurture and soothe her appropriately. When parents provide this secure base children are free to explore and enjoy their world.

Internal working models

The 'secure base' is also internalised so that it becomes a representation of security within the individual psyche. This is referred to as an 'internal working model'. These internal working models encompass what individuals expect from and feel about others and what they feel about themselves. They manifest themselves through different attachment patterns. A secure person generally feels good about themselves and others. Someone with an insecure attachment style may feel more negative about themselves and have more negative expectations and experiences of others. An insecure attachment style usually affects intimacy in adult relationships and makes it more difficult for the individual to reach out to others, form good relationships and be friendly and co-operative.

Box 2.2: Attachment styles

Secure attachment – characterised by trust in the availability, responsiveness and helpfulness of attachment figures in stressful or frightening situations.

Anxious-ambivalent – characterised by uncertainty about a caregiver's availability and responsiveness and is associated with clingy, wary and vigilant behaviour.

Avoidant – characterised by lack of confidence in an attachment figure and is associated with rejecting, distant behaviour.

Disorganised – characterised by no coherent or organised strategy for keeping a caregiver close and obtaining their care and protection.

Patterns of attachment are summarised in Box 2.2. At one end of the spectrum an individual with an avoidant attachment style is likely to play down the importance of relationships and focus on the need to be independent and self-reliant. At the other end of the spectrum, a preoccupied or ambivalent attachment style refers to a tendency towards a preoccupation with relationships. An individual with this attachment style is likely to be very clingy, overly dependent on others for self-esteem and support, and to protest when not feeling close. In the centre, an adult with a secure attachment style is likely to find it relatively easy to trust others, open up emotionally, and commit to long-term relationships (Schachner et al., 2006).

Research has found that people with insecure attachment profiles tend to be less supportive of their partners or overly anxious to please. Those with a secure attachment profile tend to compromise, take into account both their own and their partner's interests and remain more positive about the relationship in the face of conflict (Treboux et al., 2004). They are also better communicators and more likely to derive a sense of support from a partner (e.g. Cobb et al., 2001).

The development of adult attachment

Although there may be a strong link between childhood and adult attachment patterns an infant attachment pattern is not fixed for life. Rather, it can be seen as developing over time, shaped by the relationships that are experienced along the way. Good experiences as a child or adolescent can reduce the impact of early insecure attachment patterns. This process is mapped out in Figure 2.4.

Figure 2.4: Attachment and adult relationships

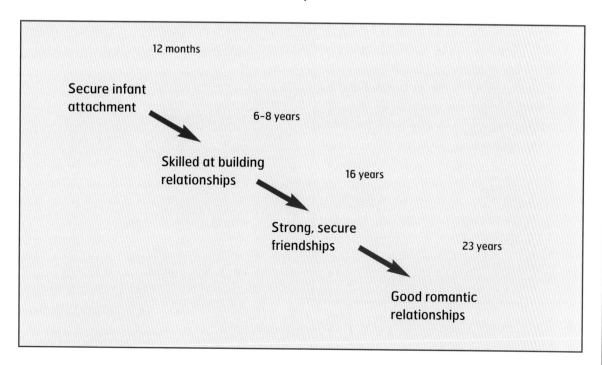

Although positive relationship experiences can moderate early attachment styles, individuals with more negative internal working models find it more difficult to form and maintain good relationships. Early experiences shape how an individual relates to his or her peers and others during childhood, which in turn predicts the kind of relationships, particularly romantic relationships, that are formed in adulthood (Simms, 2002).

However, individuals do go on to form satisfying couple relationships despite personal insecure attachment patterns (Cowan and Cowan, 2003). Where individuals achieve this they are able to create a secure base that provides the secure parenting their children need in order to thrive.

Key Messages

- Partners bring to relationships their past experiences, including their genetic inheritance, childhood experiences, and their personal traits and needs. The combination of these hidden needs and past experiences means that a relationship is much more than the sum of the two individuals in it — it is a complex and changing system.

- Whether the relationship survives is often a reflection of what partners bring, the life challenges they encounter together, and their ways of coping and relating. Couples with relatively poor ways of coping and relating usually drift apart, particularly when they experience challenging life events.

2. Being in a relationship

What does a good relationship look like?

Relationships that are working well are built on a foundation of friendship and intimacy. Partners know one another well: their hopes and dreams and likes and dislikes (Driver et al., 2003). They have managed to combine their individual life dreams, aspirations, values and ideas, and created a shared culture. They have a sense of themselves 'together' and an identity as a couple. They cope with times of stress or difference by being affectionate and supportive, by spending time together and sharing their feelings.

"We're there for each other, good things and bad things, we're company to do things together, because we do things together … I think we're just good friends."

(Linda, Newport)

Key features of healthy relationships include:

- **Commitment:** partners have a long-term view of the relationship; persevere in the face of difficulties; balance their needs as individuals and a couple; and develop a sense of 'we-ness' and connection through friendship, shared values and history.

- **Intimacy and emotional support:** physical and, in particular, psychological intimacy are core aspects of healthy relationships and are developed and strengthened over time, particularly through overcoming difficulties.

- **Communication:** couples communicate in positive and respectful ways and communication often involves humour, affection, and interest (known as positivity).

- **Think the best:** couples tend to think the best of each other and overlook, or are more accepting of, failings and negative behaviours or comments.

- **Conflict resolution:** partners understand that some conflict is inevitable; they 'fight fair' and learn to 'pick their battles'; they are better at 'repairing' the relationship after a disagreement and preventing disagreements from escalating. Violence is unacceptable.

- **Interaction and time together:** they have a good time together and find a healthy balance between 'couple time' and time spent doing their own thing.

Source: Robinson and Parker (2008)

While these couples get angry with each other they do not allow it to destroy the relationship. They avoid the contempt, belligerence and dominance that can be part and parcel of an ailing relationship.

> ### Key point:
> - Relationships change. They go through different stages of conflict and growth as partners struggle to find a balance between closeness and independence.

Relationship changes and challenges

Although research has highlighted some of the ways in which couples in 'healthy relationships' relate, all couples go through different and difficult phases. Figure 2.5 shows a scale with couples happy in their relationship at one end and distressed at the other, with a lot of ground in between.

Figure 2.5: The sliding scale of happiness

Happy

Distressed

© One Plus One 2008

At different stages of life couples will feel closer or further apart and more or less satisfied with the relationship (Karney and Bradbury, 1997). The umbrella signifies the protective factors that make for more satisfying relationships and that keep relationships working during difficult times. These include: affection, support, time together, and expressing and sharing feelings. Although it is a struggle to work through a difficult or unhappy phase in a relationship, many of the couples who stick with it do find happiness again. For example, one study found that nearly two thirds (62 per cent) of unhappily married partners who stayed together reported that their relationships were happy five years later (Waite and Luo, 2002).

"There's probably been two if not three occasions where we could have split up. Then maybe six months after the event you think, am I glad that we persevered with it because it's all got back to normal. But you can understand how marriages fail."

(Jordan, Bristol)

Relationship stages

Relationships also develop over time. These potential stages of development are shown in Figure 2.6 (developed from Kovacs, 1988). The stages show how partners strive to find a balance between wanting to be a couple and wanting to be separate individuals. It is often during the transition from one stage to another that conflict occurs, for example, as partners realise how unrealistic their expectations of one another were and start to revise them. Or when one partner starts to reassert their independence, as in the case of this couple:

"When we started I felt much older than Karen, but now she's catching up. She knows what she wants — which can be difficult for me. Karen started her course and got into it in a big way. It was too much with the baby as well. She was dead difficult to live with... I wondered if I could hack it. I was out of work at the time. Now things are better, and life has settled down again."

(Dave, Hull)

Couples do not necessarily progress smoothly from one stage to another until they reach the final stage. Events and personal development can mean couples revisit earlier stages as they continue to balance the need to be close and the need to be separate individuals.

"You get married and it's great — for the first few weeks — and then you are trying to sort out whether you've become a different person or whether you are the same. I want to be me first, as well as being married."

(Fiona, Guildford)

People often find this model helpful because it normalises the difficult phases and reminds them that things will get better. In some cultures, for example, where a marriage is arranged, the relationship may go through different stages.

Figure 2.6: Changes and stages of relationships

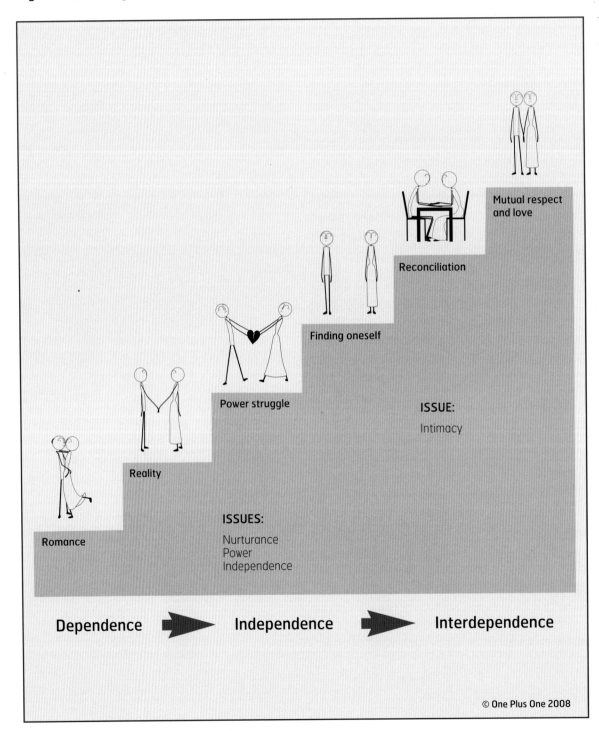

Romance

Reality

Power struggle

Finding oneself

Reconciliation

Mutual respect and love

ISSUES:
Nurturance
Power
Independence

ISSUE:
Intimacy

Dependence ➔ Independence ➔ Interdependence

© One Plus One 2008

Stage 1: Romance
– becoming a couple

Relationships usually start out with romance, though in some cultures, for example, where a marriage is arranged, romance may come later. The couple only have eyes for each other!

"We look forward to people coming but we are glad when they eventually go because we do like to be on our own quite a bit... We don't go out very much ... we like being together, living together, just the things married people do I suppose."

(Stephen, Lincoln)

At this stage they are building a sense of togetherness, so differences and difficulties are often overlooked, even denied. Everything is perfect – it feels quite 'unreal' – and in a way it is. But couples need this intense phase, and if they do not build this 'togetherness', the relationship can run into difficulties very quickly.

Stage 2: Reality
– the differences start to appear

Reality hits eventually and partners each reconnect with the outside world and realise again they are two individuals with differences that have to be reconciled. It can be a disillusioning time. Each partner has to adjust to the responsibilities, problems and complexity of living together. This includes learning how to compromise, managing conflict and working through differences.

"It sounds stupid now, but I thought married life would continue as before. But things change and you change. I have changed so much since I married. When we first got married I looked up to John. Now I question things more."

(Liz, St Albans)

Some couples are frightened by how the relationship begins to change. And if one partner begins to re-establish their independence the other may become very clingy. Partners who manage this phase well have a much better chance of developing the skills they need in order to deal with the challenges of the coming years.

Stage 3: Power struggles
– practising independence

It's at this stage that Power Struggles occur - each partner is growing in independence and wanting to get their own way, perhaps out of a fear of not being accepted or respected by the other. Arguments, blaming and criticism become more frequent and intense; conflict rises and is often focused on issues such as money, bringing up the children and who does what around the home.

"We went through a stage where we argued an awful lot; we couldn't walk home without arguing - we could keep to the subject of 'dogs' and still end up arguing. We even argued about which dog we were going to have when we married."

(Sue, Bangor)

This is a difficult stage for couples and a time when some relationships break down. But many couples work though this stage by coming to terms with their differences and finding ways of not letting their disagreements damage their closeness, even though they struggle to keep a sense of connection.

Stage 4: Finding oneself
– independence

The next stage is another difficult one for couples - when one or both partners are engaged in 'finding oneself' in some way again. The focus shifts away from 'we' – to 'me' as individuals each question: 'Who am I?' 'What do I want?' 'What do I need?'

"We found more space as we went on ... to do with little things e.g. reading at night rather than cuddling... there was a finding a space ... that was about half way through (15 years ago) at first being anxious because of lack of a closeness and then quite welcoming it."

(Katy, Trowbridge)

Couples often find this stage particularly stressful because they feel less connected and sense that they are drifting apart because both are doing their own thing. They may argue more and it is often at this stage that one or other has an affair, or couples decide to separate. Partners resolve things when they are able to reconnect without losing their identity.

Stage 5: Reconciliation – working through

Couples who have weathered the difficult stages can accept the independence of their partner and still feel connected to them. So they focus on reconciliation as they work out a new sense of togetherness. They understand each other better, are more accepting and tolerant of each other and feel committed. They see their differences as a strength and not a weakness in their relationship.

"Both of us have got our independence, but we've also got the closeness of each other as well together. We've got our lives apart and our lives together, which blends together brilliantly, it really does."

(Jackie, Chelmsford)

Stage 6: Mutual respect and love - interdependence

Mutual respect and love is the final stage and one that all couples aspire to - some even get there, if only for a moment! Each partner feels fully accepted by the other – warts and all. After 25 years together Brenda can see that:

"You start to appreciate the strengths of your partner ... and so you begin to understand that those things are good and therefore you are more accepting of the other things."

(Brenda, Liverpool)

They have reached a comfortable balance between togetherness and separateness. Both partners are free to explore new ways of fulfilling themselves instead of pouring so much energy into the relationship.

Difference and conflict

Conflict often arises as partners navigate the different stages of their relationship. Conflict is a normal and necessary part of family life and an important way of resolving differences – particularly in the early years. The 'enduring vulnerabilities' each partner brings to the relationship makes difference and disagreement inevitable.

"Most of it is about differentness ... that we are different ... and there is such a struggle to accommodate someone else."

(John, Chester)

Accepting each other's strengths, limitations and vulnerabilities is part of helping the relationship to grow.

What do couples argue about?

Couples argue about a range of things. Top issues include: finances, the in-laws, disciplining children, 'who does what' around the home (particularly in the postnatal period) and sex (www.onepoll.com). Couples are more likely to argue at times of stress or important life transitions, such as when money is scarce, when a family member is ill, when a new baby comes along, or when one partner is unemployed (Simons, 1999). Diary studies show that conflict is worse on days of high general life stress than on other days (Fincham, 2003). An individual who has had a difficult day at work is more likely to get caught up in conflict at home.

Arguments about some subjects are associated with a greater likelihood of divorce, such as extramarital sex, substance abuse, wives' reports of their partner's jealously, and spending money foolishly (Fincham, 2003). But, invariably, topics are a smoke-screen for more fundamental, underlying issues such as fears about the loss of identity, or threats to a partner's values (Gutteridge, 2003). As Jamal recognises:

"So when you ask me if I have come across any big things, big problems – yeah, I have come across big things but not because of the thing itself, but because it is about the relationship, and that is massive. That is really big."

(Jamal, Nottingham)

Conflict is a necessary part of working through these underlying issues. How partners manage conflict, rather than conflict itself, is what matters to the relationship. When partners are handling conflict well it tends to stimulate problem-solving discussion and act as a powerful motivator for change. Conflict can be more destructive when the tension or compromises it involves threaten the identity needs of both partners. When this happens it triggers partners' defensive responses. Then conflict is used to keep a partner at a distance (Gutteridge, 2003). Common defensive responses are 'fight', 'flight' or 'freeze'.

A fight response means that a partner goes on the attack when the other partner raises an issue. Arguments can easily escalate. The 'flight' or 'freeze' response means that a partner tries to defend himself from the threat raised by conflict by withdrawing or 'stonewalling'. This might mean they shut down and go quiet, or leave the room. If this 'flight' pattern continues partners can get stuck in the 'demand-withdraw' pattern. Which means that whenever one partner, usually the female partner, raises an issue, the other partner always backs off and either fails or refuses to respond, maybe even leaving the room.

"He wouldn't talk. He would actually storm out of the house and slam the door rather than have a discussion about anything."

(Gayathri, Sandwell)

The features of troubled relationships

Although these are common responses to conflict, they can push partners apart and make it difficult to sort things out. As partners fail to communicate,

> **Key points:**
> - Conflict is inevitable. It is invariably a symptom of deeper, underlying issues around power or personal identity.
> - Conflict need not be destructive if partners find ways of handling it well.

hurts remain unforgiven and unresolved and partners cease to be close. Partners end up exchanging more harsh words and fewer kind ones. They start to think the worst (see Box 2.3). They often 'give as good as they get!' so that the row or sulking escalates. One minute a couple may be arguing about the washing-up, and the next they are talking about divorce. Bottling things up does not help either. It usually means that a partner becomes resentful and explodes when they reach the 'last straw' anyway.

"I wish she'd say when she isn't happy so I could do something. I think things are alright and then whoosh she explodes... then it's a million things that she has been saving up to cover me in. And though she might have a point I'm not going to say that am I?"

(Paul, Loughborough)

Although both partners may realise that what they are doing is not helpful it becomes a hard habit to break (e.g. Bradbury et al., 2004).

These troubled relationships are invariably characterised by what John Gottman, who has made a life's work of studying couple relationships, calls the four horsemen of the Apocalypse. These are:

- contempt;
- criticism;
- defensiveness; and
- stonewalling (either physical or emotional withdrawal).

Some of these patterns are apparent in Jill's relationship. Her partner left shortly after this difficult phase:

"At that point, things had changed from having a husband who was so attentive and loving and caring and all of that to somebody who just shut down. I had been so proud of him, and me. I really thought that I had the perfect man. But he says that there wasn't any change. He just says that it is because my expectations are very high and if I learn to calm down a bit everything would be hunky dory."

(Jill, London)

Gender differences often become more pronounced when relationships are under stress. For example, women tend to be more critical and men more stonewalling. This was Laura's experience:

"But I feel that a lot of the time he doesn't listen to me. It all makes me upset. I have seriously thought about leaving for the last couple of months, I have to say."

(Laura, Liverpool)

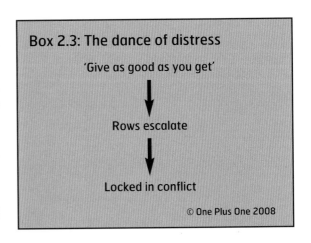

Box 2.3: The dance of distress

'Give as good as you get'

↓

Rows escalate

↓

Locked in conflict

© One Plus One 2008

Figure 2.7: Hidden Issues

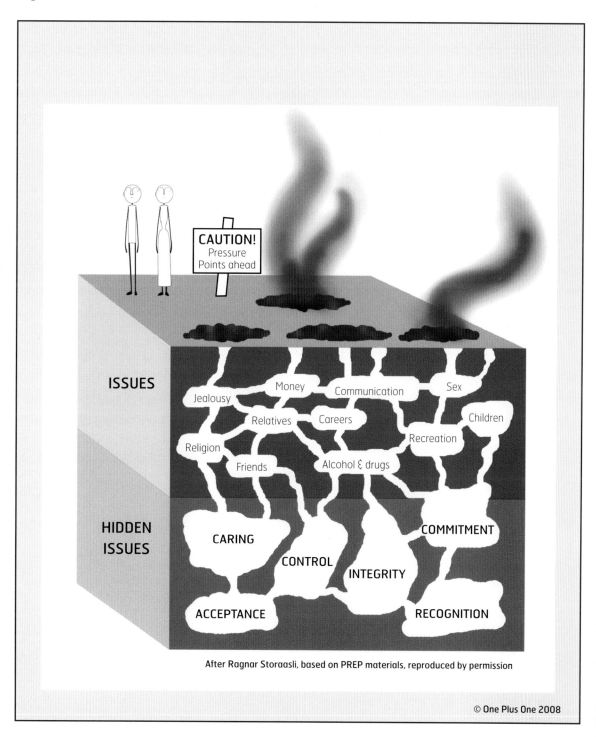

After Ragnar Storaasli, based on PREP materials, reproduced by permission

© One Plus One 2008

How couples manage conflict in happy relationships

As 70 per cent of arguments are about the same issues partners have to find healthy ways of dealing with their ongoing differences (Driver et al, 2003).

This couple have found their own way:

"Sometimes when times are difficult you feel like you are revisiting the 'same old same old' issues again. But rather than get angry about that, we say to ourselves that that is the universe telling us that we didn't really deal with the issue properly before. We remind ourselves of that."

(Dan and Liz, Norwich)

When couples argue in ways that do not destroy the relationship their arguments are characterised by the following:

- the woman brings up a problem gently rather than charging in aggressively. This is critical as it is usually women who raise concerns about the relationship;
- the male partner is willing to accept his partner's point of view rather than 'batting back' her ideas and suggestions straight away;
- partners seek to keep the relationship on track during conflict. For example, one partner might say, 'The problem is, I don't think either one of us is paying much attention to what is important to the other!';
- they hold on to the positives during conflict. When couples in healthy relationships argue they manage to have at least five 'positive' exchanges for every negative one, such as expressions of humour, affection or warmth. Couples in troubled relationships have just one positive expression for every negative one, or even less than that; and

- they compromise and they forgive one another.

(Source: Gottman, 1994a; Bradbury et al., 2004)

Same but different

Although research suggests there are ways of dealing with conflict that are less harmful to a relationship, that does not mean that all relationships are the same. Happy couples are diverse. Some couples have very little conflict in their relationship and generally agree to differ. Other relationships may be very passionate and full of intensity. Compare these two couples:

"Our life has been one long argument - morning, noon and night! We argue for breakfast, lunch and dinner. We argue about everything. We bicker, argue, yell, though there's never been any physical violence at all".

(Andrew, Stockport)

"We don't really have an argumentative relationship. We will bicker maybe, and though I hate to say it I am the one who stands their ground. I'll think "No, hang on a minute" and tell him what I think. He is normally the one who says sorry in the end, although if I am in the wrong I do admit to it."

(Hazel, Morpeth)

What happy couples share, however, is a healthy balance so that even when they argue couples hold on to positive ways of relating (Driver et al., 2003).

Virtuous and vicious cycles: support matters too...

Much of the focus in this section has been on conflict between partners. Conflict is important and is often an indicator of underlying relationship problems, but support matters too. Support affects how happy couples are in the relationship (Fincham, 2003). The positive ways in which partners relate to each other e.g. confiding in one another, differentiates between couples whose relationships survive and those whose relationships break down. Couples who begin to lose the love and affection they shared are at greater risk of splitting up than those couples who find themselves fighting more (Huston and Melz, 2004). Ellie's relationship went through a difficult phase after her mother died:

"I think like I became quite cold, insular. And it was due to grief, you know, it was a kind of something else going wrong in my life and I think he just couldn't understand it, and I think, I suppose like I blamed him because he couldn't understand how I felt."

(Ellie, Reading)

The support couples provide to one another helps them to build trust. It also helps them to interpret their partners' behaviour in a positive light. For example, a thoughtless comment is not seen as being driven by a partner's malice but by less harmful factors, such as tiredness or a bad day. Researchers think that these positives protect the couple so that the less supportive things they do and say do not have a lasting impact on their happiness in the relationship (Bradbury and Karney, 2004).

Figure 2.8 (on page 46) illustrates the 'vicious cycles' of relating that partners can get trapped in and the 'virtuous cycles' that help to keep couples together. They demonstrate how important a partner's support is during difficult times.

Key point:
- The support partners provide to one another protects the relationship from the impact of more negative behaviours such as criticism.

Figure 2.8: Virtuous and vicious cycles of relating

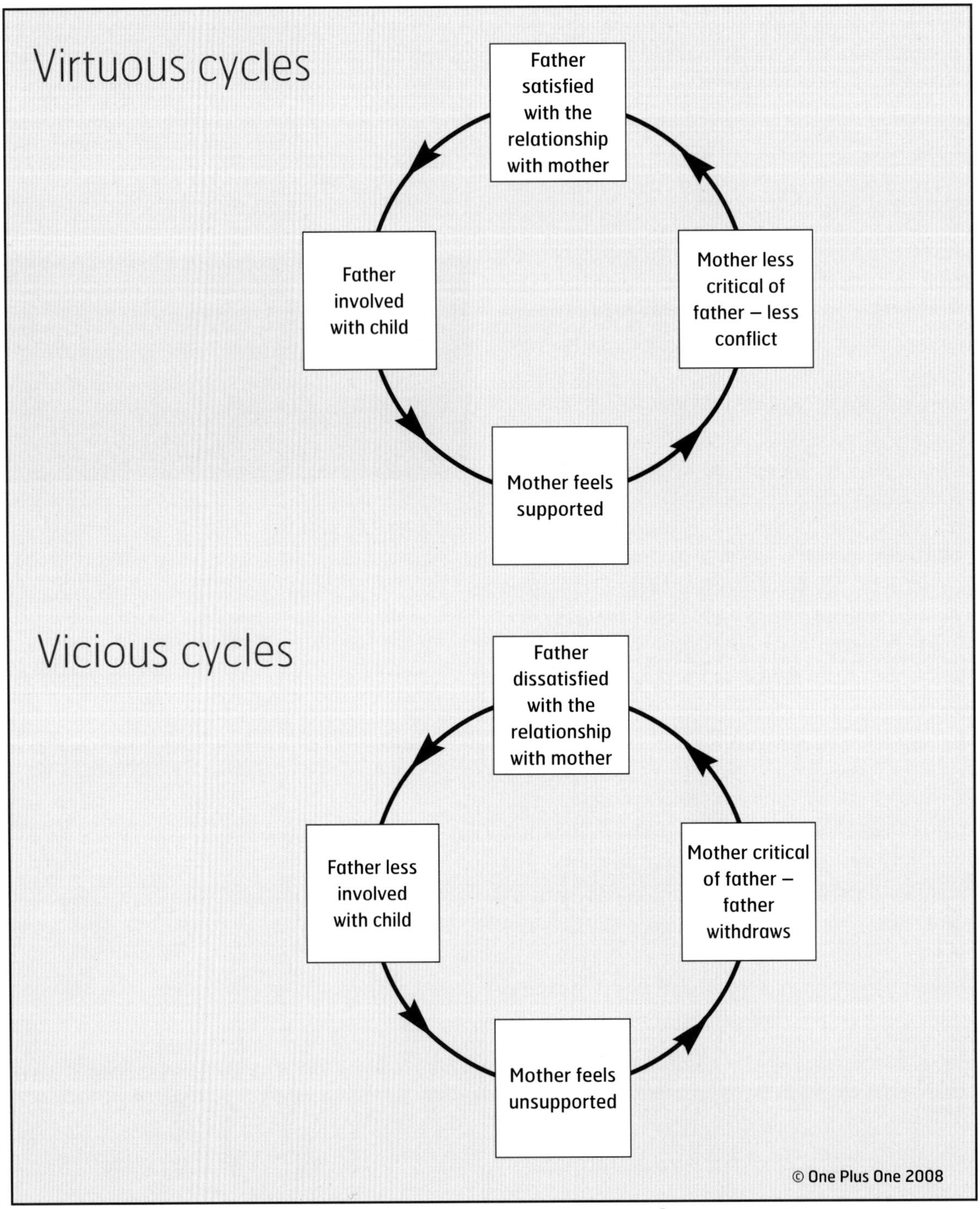

Virtuous cycles

- Father satisfied with the relationship with mother
- Mother less critical of father – less conflict
- Mother feels supported
- Father involved with child

Vicious cycles

- Father dissatisfied with the relationship with mother
- Mother critical of father – father withdraws
- Mother feels unsupported
- Father less involved with child

© One Plus One 2008

Differences between men and women

The emotional character of the relationship is invariably more important to how happy women are in a relationship than men (e.g. see Erickson, 1993; Wilkie et al., 1998). The effort men put in to the relationship – their 'emotion work' – has a strong influence on how satisfied women are in a relationship. In one study, men's emotion work, such as apologising after an argument, discussing problems, and expressing affection, was more important to the quality of the relationship than a range of other factors that predict relationship happiness, such as how partners share household tasks and how happy they are with the arrangement (Wilcox and Nock, 2006).

Conflicting needs?

Communication with her partner is important to a woman's sense of satisfaction in the relationship. But there can be a tension between the woman's desire to talk abut the relationship and a man's desire to avoid it. Women are more likely to identify problems, to want to talk about them and to want to resolve them, including through seeking changes in her partner. Men, in general, tend to see talking about the relationship as indicative of problems and are uncomfortable talking about issues. They are more likely to minimize problems, avoid conflict and seek reconciliation (Suh et al., 2004).

A woman is likely to find the failure to talk about relationship issues a problem in itself (Duck and Wood, 2005) and women who see a decline in communication with their partner can become dissatisfied with the relationship (Riessman, 1990). Toby was aware of how his partner struggled with the way in which he kept things to himself.

"She says to me, 'you never open up to me'. She says 'I tell you everything'. She said, 'but you, you, if you've got a problem, you don't say anything.' I said, 'well that's just the way I am. I've never been any different, it's just the way I am."

(Toby, London)

When things are going wrong, women are also more prone to brood on difficulties and get caught up in their negative feelings. This often serves to sustain or amplify them (Schulz et al., 2004). In contrast, men are more likely to become dissatisfied when they are involved in fewer activities with their partner. Gender differences in how men and women relate become more apparent when couples are under stress (Schulz et al., 2004).

Key Messages

- The course of a relationship is invariably shaped by the combination of traits and past experiences partners bring to the relationship and how they communicate about and cope with the difficult life events they encounter.

- How they navigate the journey from romance to reality is also important. If partners cannot find ways to accommodate the ongoing, conflicting needs of intimacy and independence they are likely to encounter difficulties.

- Conflict is necessary and healthy. But there are ways of arguing that signify trouble for a relationship. For example, couples who treat each other with contempt, who cannot find ways to stop conflict from escalating or a kind word to say, and where one partner withdraws as soon as the other partner raises a concern are at risk of relationship breakdown.

- Support is also important. The quality of the support partners offer to one another is more important than their experiences of conflict.

3. Relationships under pressure

Couples coping with difficult events and circumstances are particularly vulnerable to falling into the negative cycles of relating described in the previous section. Some common challenges are described in this section, which covers situations such as economic stress, ill-health and infidelity. Even change itself – transition – can be stressful because it creates uncertainty and insecurity. That is why one of the most common life transitions for couples – becoming parents – is included in this section. As Figure 2.2 at the beginning of this section on couple relationships illustrated, how couples cope with these external pressures is affected by what they bring to the relationship and the communication skills and coping resources they have developed together. Outside help is important and the support and information that well placed practitioners can provide is crucial.

The following sections provide a summary of the research. As such they create a composite picture of the challenges couples in these circumstances can face. They are not exhaustive and are designed to expand understanding of relationships, not confine it to a stereotypical picture of a relationship under pressure.

The roller coaster of change

Coping with stressful events can feel like a 'roller coaster of change' (see Figure 2.9). When things are going smoothly, couples have established patterns of relating. They have worked out individual roles and responsibility for household chores, decisions about how to spend their time, how they relate to one another, power struggles, and ways of staying close.

Figure 2.9: The roller coaster of change

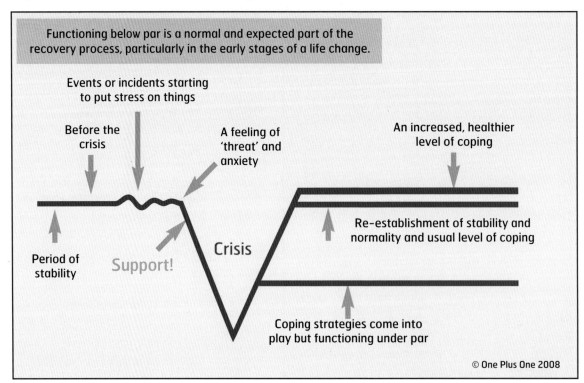

Functioning below par is a normal and expected part of the recovery process, particularly in the early stages of a life change.

Events or incidents starting to put stress on things

Before the crisis

A feeling of 'threat' and anxiety

An increased, healthier level of coping

Period of stability

Support!

Crisis

Re-establishment of stability and normality and usual level of coping

Coping strategies come into play but functioning under par

© One Plus One 2008

However, a crisis often overturns these established patterns. Some people become anxious, and feel unable to cope. They may even feel hopeless as their usual way of dealing with problems fail and they struggle to find new ways to cope. As they feel the stress, some partners will start to see and believe the worst of one another. Over time, this can undermine how happy they are in the relationship (Neff and Karney, 2004). For Pete, work stress took its toll on his relationship:

"I changed my job in our relationship because I was finding that because of the career I was taking, that I was working all hours and my partner began to resent that. And it got to the point where she would sit there and be thinking 'oh god when is he going to be coming home' and you think 'I just don't want to go home because all I'm going to get is moaned at.' I think recognising that is the hardest thing."

(Pete, Billericay)

But research also demonstrates how resilient many couples are in the face of great stress and their capacity to develop strategies that help each other cope with what life throws at them. For this couple, troubles brought them closer together:

"When we got married I thought, don't let anything go wrong. But they have – money problems, employment problems... But we've got an extra something from knowing we got through things, together. Now I know we are committed – before, I just hoped we would be."

(Ngosi, Hull)

Key points:

- Stressful events challenge couples' coping mechanisms and communication skills.
- If couples struggle to cope they are vulnerable to falling into harmful communication cycles.

Becoming parents

- 50 per cent of new parents surveyed reported a severe or moderate decline in relationship satisfaction.
- Only 19 per cent felt that it improved the relationship (Belsky and Kelly, 1994).

Becoming parents is one of the most common but challenging experiences that couples experience in the course of their relationship. As couples deal with the changes that new parenthood brings they often experience a drop in relationship satisfaction (Belsky and Kelly, 1994; Lawrence et al., 2008). Some of this may be explained by couples' high levels of satisfaction with the relationship during pregnancy and a drop as they reach the end of a 'honeymoon period' (Perren et al., 2005). But it is also a response to the pressures they come under as they adjust to new parenthood. This couple's experience is typical of what some new parents go through:

"Once we became parents everything changed: we argued like we never argued before, about trivial things really. But somehow we started to feel different about each other, like we were no longer on the same side. I was frightened things would get worse. My health visitor picked up that I was anxious and I poured it all out to her. She said many couples feel like this and it's important to talk to each other. When I started to tell Joe how I felt he looked so relieved. We had both been bottling it up."

(Rachel, Manchester)

Many couples find themselves arguing much more over this time, as well as failing to be as warm, supportive and affectionate as they used to be (Spanier et al., 1983; Cowan and Cowan, 2000). Holding on to these more positive ways of relating is key to keeping the relationship on track.

An important element of a couple's adjustment is the co-parenting relationship they establish. This reflects how they manage their parenting e.g. the support or lack of it they provide one another and the level of conflict they experience over childrearing (Feinberg and Kan, 2008). One aspect of this is how much they share the joys of parenting – observing how they each grow into the role of parent and celebrate their children's development together (Feinberg, 2002). As partners prepare for and adapt to their roles as parents they are very receptive to support in building the co-parental relationship.

Relationship challenges and processes

Parents face a number of challenges as they adjust to new parenthood that explain why relationships come under pressure.

Managing the pressures

Most obviously, partners have less time for one another. They often put their relationship on hold while they grapple with tiredness and anxiety, and juggle family and work life demands. They also lack the time and opportunity to nurture the relationship (Cowan and Cowan, 2003). But parents are also adjusting to more complex changes.

Establishing a new balance

Moving from two in the family to three (or more) changes how each member of the family relates to the other. For example, partners have to revise the balance of giving and receiving and how they meet each others' needs for affection and esteem (Veroff et al., 2000). Partners can be left struggling to understand why their perceived needs are not being met (Belsky and Kelly, 1994), something this new mother recognised:

"Communication is so important. Someone new comes into your life and you have to reassess your

relationship. You need to talk to each other about these tensions before they take hold."

(Ginny, Sheffield)

Changing roles and identities

Men and women also need to develop a sense of themselves as parents. In order to take on their parental identities, women think of themselves less as a partner or lover and more as a parent. Men's sense of themselves as a partner/ lover also shrinks, but to a much lesser extent, and, on average, parenthood takes up less mental space for men than it does for women (Cowan and Cowan, 2000). This was the experience of Sarah:

"I don't think Derek has changed at all to be honest. I don't think he feels that it is up to him. I feel that my identity has had to change because I am a mum and have had to cope with all this. Sometimes I feel I have failed in some way. Actually, I feel like my identity has been changed for me rather than anything else – I feel very much that I have changed and adapted and coped with things."

(Sarah, Birmingham)

Researchers have found that the greater the difference between men and women in their sense of themselves as parents when their babies are six months old, the less satisfied both partners are with the relationship over the course of the following year (Cowan et al., 1991).

Key point:

- Relationships come under pressure when partners become parents. Challenges include: negotiating new roles and responsibilities; finding new ways to meet each other's needs; and coping with a loss of sexual intimacy.

Part of this adjustment involves dividing up household responsibilities differently – particularly where couples previously shared household tasks. In most cases, women take on more traditional roles. Women who had more egalitarian arrangements before the baby can feel unhappy as they find themselves slipping into a 'traditional' relationship (Belsky et al., 1986). Problems also arise when partners' expectations are different from postnatal reality, particularly when a new mother had expected a partner to be more involved in family life than he turned out to be (Kluwer et al., 1997).

"My role became purely that of a mother. I don't think he was even thinking of me as a wife at that point. The first year he was basically away and he came home only at weekends. I was just the housewife and the mother at that point, and because I wasn't working I shoved all the challenges I needed and had previously got through work onto bringing up the girls. I taught them to read very early on, for example. All my 'subdued stuff' – my needs – I shoved through the girls."

(Karen, London)

Getting out of sync

Men and women also adjust to changes in their relationships at different rates. On average, women's relationship satisfaction declines from pregnancy through the first year of parenthood, with the peak decline in the first 6 months after the birth. For men, these changes are later, and relationship satisfaction often declines in the second year of the infant's life (Cowan and Cowan, 2003).

Loss of sexual intimacy

Tiredness, discomfort and a traumatic delivery can all take their toll on sexual intimacy. A disrupted sex life is common. Some women find it difficult to come to terms with how their bodies have changed and may feel unattractive or worried about their shape. Men may also find it difficult to cope with a partner's physical and emotional changes or may be struggling with the experience of the birth. Couples can easily fall out of sync and must find a way to meet each other's needs for inclusion and intimacy when one partner is not ready to resume sexual intimacy (d'Ardenne and Morrod, 2003).

"Well there's this sexual thing at the moment... we don't exactly have rows but I just don't feel in charge of my body any more, it belongs to everybody else. They all want to use it in their own ways... I just want to go to bed and sleep because I don't know when I'm going to have to get up, and how many times."

(Natasha, Glasgow)

(See section on 'Sexual difficulties' on page 68 for more general information.)

Which relationships are most vulnerable?

Some parents are at greater risk of experiencing problems in their relationship as they adjust to parenthood than others. Some key risk factors include:

- **Pre-existing problems** – The arrival of a new baby usually exacerbates pre-existing problems (Lawrence et al., 2008). Couples who have a baby to rekindle the relationship often get driven further apart.

- **Disagreements about whether to start a family** – If the female partner gets pregnant in the knowledge that her partner is not willing to start a family, partners are more likely to experience a drop in relationship satisfaction (Lawrence et al., 2008) or to separate after the birth (Cowan and Cowan, 2000).

- **Poor experiences in the family of origin** – Parents who grew up in homes marked by conflict between their parents are more likely to experience problems in their own relationship following a birth. Partners stressed by the challenge of caring for a new baby can adopt the unhelpful ways of relating that they learnt in childhood (Lane et al., 1988; Perren et al., 2005).

- **Economic privilege** – A statistical review of studies found that parents in higher socio-economic groups were less satisfied with their relationships over the postnatal period than those in other groups (Twenge et al., 2003). One reason is the bigger adjustment these parents have to make, particularly where the mother had a successful career. Having a baby means adjusting to more traditional roles and lifestyles that are constrained by caring commitments.

- **Insufficient resources** – At the other end of the spectrum, couples who have been termed as 'fragile families' are also at risk. These are unmarried parents, often very young, who live on or near the poverty line. These young families often do not have access to the emotional, financial and social resources they need to manage their relationships over the transition to parenthood (Carlson and McLanahan, 2006).

- **Psychological disturbance** – Relationship difficulties also often coexist with postnatal depression. Postnatal depression is discussed in the later section on depression (see page 58).

Caring for children with disabilities

- More than half a million children in England have a mild to seriously disabling condition or chronic illness.
- 78 per cent of parents caring for a child with profound and multiple learning disabilities received either no support or less than 2 hours a week – 20 minutes a day – to help them with their caring tasks; tasks that are invariably round the clock (Mencap, 2001).

On top of the usual challenges associated with becoming parents, parents caring for a child with a disability often have to cope with financial pressures, lack of time, guilt and blame, and worries about the child's health, well-being and care. Although some parents find these pressures bring them together, others struggle to cope and can find themselves being driven apart[3].

Relationship patterns and challenges
His and her roles

Parents caring for a child with a disability often adopt traditional gender roles which reflect differences in each partner's earning power as well as assumptions about who is best suited to a caring role. In many cases, these roles become entrenched and partners end up feeling overburdened or unhappy with how tasks have been divided up (Wiegner and Donders, 2000; Rydström, et al., 2004), as this parent explains:

"Any difficulties between my husband and I are exacerbated by the additional stress and time lost to caring for a disabled child. Neither of us gets enough time and attention for us as individuals and neither of us has the capacity to give more to the

3. Section based on the findings of a review into the impact of caring for a disabled child on the couple relationship (Glenn, 2007)

other. There is a great deal of resentment – he resents that I don't spend as much time with our disabled child as he does, and I resent that he doesn't recognise the colossal effort I put into co-ordinating schedules, visiting school and fighting continuous battles to get what our son needs."

(Sarah, Worcester)[4]

Lack of time

Parents caring for a child with a disability have little time for themselves, other siblings or their relationship. Children with some disorders require a significant amount of care day and night. As one parent is often unable to work because of the complex care needs of their child, the other parent may work long hours to boost the family income. In one study, 90 per cent of parents of a child with learning disabilities said they did not have enough time together (Bauman, 2004).

Financial strain

Financial pressures place a strain on a relationship. Economic worries can leave parents feeling depressed and demoralised with a knock-on impact on the relationship and their parenting (Conger et al., 1992).

Support and coping

Couples' responses to these pressures vary. One important factor is coping style, which affects an individual's ability to draw support from a partner as well as their ability to handle the pressures and circumstances of their caring responsibilities. Some people cope by focusing on the problem and finding solutions or strategies to improve it. Other people focus on finding ways to feel better about a situation by reinterpreting it, distancing themselves, or even denying or avoiding it. Partners can find these differences frustrating and it is important to recognise and acknowledge each partner's coping strategies. Couples are likely to do best if they can adopt a problem-focused coping style – which means finding practical ways to reduce stress. This couple drew on each other and their faith:

"We made a very good team. We bounced off each other a lot. There were a lot of tears back then. We prayed a lot together and tried to stay strong. We tried to be very, very positive. We didn't ask people to come round and see us – we managed it on our own."

(Ben, Harrogate)

Supportive partners can protect one another from parenting stresses. They can also protect one another from the risk of depression associated with caring for a child with a disability.

Outside support can also make a difference.

"Talking about a relationship issue can have an enormous impact on the family. We have seen people who e.g. have children with ADHD where the mother feels that she is not getting as much support as she could do. In these kinds of cases, actually just for us to acknowledge that fact and how difficult it is allows them to acknowledge that they are not mad. The big thing is that it can encourage them to talk to their partner more, and we can also help them by signposting to other services."

(Health Visitor)

Where couples cannot manage these pressures, or lack sufficient support to deal with them, they often get trapped in destructive ways of relating. If mothers feel unsupported the relationship can crumble as the father withdraws in response to criticism about his contribution. The mother is usually left feeling even more unsupported as she copes with often challenging behaviour from the children as they pick up on problems between the parents.

4. Source: Contact a Family, 2004.

Which relationships are most vulnerable?

Some relationships are more vulnerable than others. Risk factors include:

- **Pre-existing difficulties** – Pre-existing relationship problems appear to be a key factor in explaining relationship instability postnatally. As one parent says:

"In my view a disabled child in the family strengthens a good marriage but shows up any flaws in a way nothing else would in a bad marriage."

(Liz, Redcar).

- **The disorder and its severity** – Relationships come under different types and levels of pressure according to their child's disorder and its severity (Berant et al., 2003; Joesch and Smith, 1997). Specific disorders involve different caring demands and social stigmas and help to explain differences in how well couples cope.

Key points:

- Parents caring for a child with a disability often face considerable pressures including: lack of time for one another; dealing with the grief over the loss of the 'hoped' for baby; financial strain and coping with constraining roles and responsibilities resulting from extensive care demands.
- Developing effective and compatible coping skills and harnessing the support of those around them can protect couples in the face of these pressures.

When one partner is seriously ill

In a survey of cancer sufferers and their partners:

- Over two-thirds of respondents said that one of them being unwell had put a strain on their relationship.
- One fifth of participants felt they coped badly with these strains, although others (43 per cent) fared better.
- Despite the strain, most couples stay together in the face of serious illness (Cutrona, 1996). Just four per cent of couples in the survey of cancer sufferers broke up with their partner.

(Cancerbackup and Relate, 2008).

Relationships where one partner suffers with chronic ill-health can operate under a great strain (Cutrona, 1996). Chronic illness changes how couples see each other, how they see the world and their role in it, and how the world perceives them (d'Ardenne and Morrod, 2003). Figure 2.10 summarises the links between ill-health and relationship problems. Although this section focuses on the impact of ill-health on the relationship, relationship problems can also precede ill-health (See: e.g. McAllister, 1995; Coleman and Glenn, forthcoming). Couples who lack the resources to cope with these pressures can get trapped in a cycle of ineffective coping mechanisms, poor communication, dissatisfaction with the relationship, and distress and conflict (Corney, 2005.)

Figure 2.10. Linking ill-health and troubled relationships

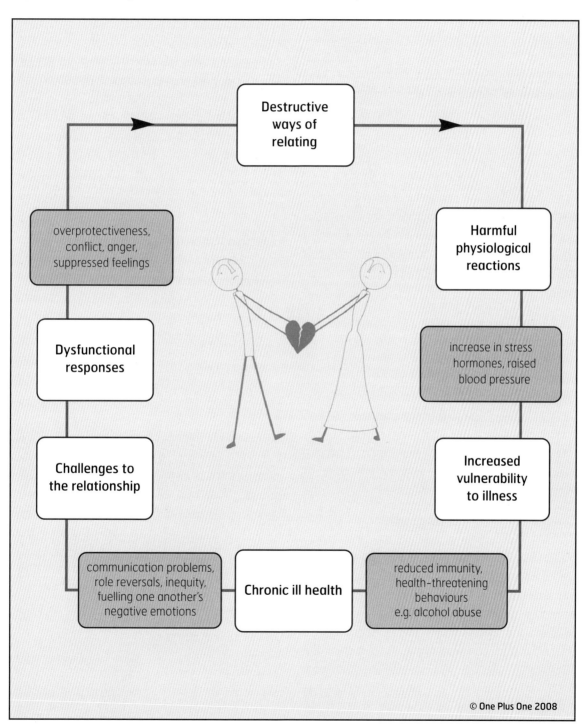

© One Plus One 2008

Relationship patterns and challenges

Managing the feelings

Both partners are vulnerable to the psychological impact of ill-health (Coyne et al., 1990). Feelings similar to bereavement, such as grief, anger and depression are common (d'Ardenne and Morrod, 2003). The ill partner may be irritable and hard to please. The well partner may feel angry and resentful but also feel guilty at having those feelings.

"And she is always on about the pain so she gets a bit grumpy at times and it interrupts her sleep ... But it's like everything else, you learn to live with it... I am learning to live with the consequences of it. But the first year or two was a bit hard."

(Anil, Durham)

Although one partner may hide their angry feelings from the other, the risk is that both partners will become emotionally isolated and lacking in support. On the other hand, one partner's angry feelings can trigger resentment or other strong feelings in the other partner. Couples need to find constructive ways to manage their feelings so that they avoid undermining the relationship (Cutrona, 1996). If they fail to do so they are likely to experience problems at a later date.

Communication and coping styles

Couples who remain happier in the relationship often have good communication skills and more helpful coping styles (Cutrona, 1996). They engage with feelings and issues, rather than adopt less helpful approaches, such as being overprotective (Bodenmann, 2005). Failing to talk about worries and difficulties can undermine the value of the relationship to its partners and prevent them from understanding each others' perspectives. Eve has continued to struggle with the way in which her partner shuts himself down and shuts her out:

"When I look back now I think I was so stupid – I thought he would really realise that I loved him by sticking by him when he was so ill. He has said thank you once or twice. I think he may feel embarrassed talking about that time because he sees his emotions as a sign of weakness. I think he recognises that he did some bad things and that he knows what he should be doing. And because he knows, and he is not doing it, that embarrasses him as well."

(Eve, Worcester)

Keeping a fair balance

Illness changes the emotional balance of a relationship. For example, as links with the outside world become limited the relationship often becomes more important to the ill partner but less important to a well partner. And, ill partners are usually more satisfied with the relationship than the well partner (O'Connor et al., 2008).

It also changes the physical balance. An ill partner is often reliant on a well partner for physical care, the running of the house, the care of the children, and financial support. Couples adopt different strategies for adjusting to this new balance. For example, they may use a different measure of fairness that takes account of all a partner has done in the past, such as raising the children. Couples who were previously happy in the relationship are more able to do this than those who were already experiencing relationship difficulties (Cutrona, 1996).

Loss of sexual intimacy

Ill health can also affect sexual intimacy. Factors arising out of the condition itself, or factors associated with it, such as tiredness, pain, and lack of desire, can make sexual activity impossible.

Psychological issues can also be important. For example, the ill partner might feel unattractive. A well partner may feel guilty seeking sexual intimacy. Or a partner might be concerned about the impact of sexual activity on the ill partner's health, for example, where a partner has a heart condition.

Different perspectives

Partners also have to manage different perceptions about the nature and course of an illness. For example, a partner suffering from breast cancer may continue to feel worried about whether the disease will recur even though treatment seems to have been a success. The well partner might struggle with this and be ready to move on to a new stage in the belief that their partner is 'cured'. Couples who cannot understand one another's perspectives risk misjudging one another's needs and fuelling resentment and emotional isolation (Cutrona, 1996).

Which relationships are most vulnerable?

Researchers have identified a number of factors that indicate where a relationship may be more vulnerable to pressure. Risk factors for those facing chronic illness include:

- **A poor relationship prior to diagnosis** – Couples who already have a poor relationship, and lack the emotional and coping resources available to those in a supportive relationship, are most at risk of relationship difficulties (Cutrona, 1996; Corney, 2005).

- **Different conditions** – The impact of chronic ill health on a relationship can vary according to the disease. For example, chronic pain disorders and cognitive impairments appear to be more damaging to the relationship than other illnesses (Cutrona, 1996). Some illnesses, such as breast cancer, can undermine a partner's body-image and have a significant impact on sexual intimacy. Other illnesses, such as rheumatoid arthritis, affect a partner's ability to contribute to household tasks and have a more significant impact on the balance of roles and responsibilities in the relationship.

- **Gender differences** – Women tend to be more distressed by chronic ill health whether they are the caregiver or the ill partner (Hagedoorn et al., 2008).

Key points:

- Couples coping with chronic illness face significant challenges.

- They have to adopt new roles; one partner usually takes on more responsibility for looking after the home and both partners have to accept the imbalance of support and manage feelings of anger, grief and loss.

- Again, communication and coping skills are vital.

Depression and couple relationships

> - Individuals in an unhappy relationship are 25 times more likely to develop clinical depression compared with those in untroubled partnerships (Weissman, 1987).

It can be difficult to untangle where relationship distress and depression begin and end (Mead, 2002). Relationship problems can trigger depression in one or both partners (Banawan et al., 2002). On the other hand, relationships where one partner is depressed are more likely to break down (Wade and Prevalin, 2004). And, unsurprisingly, depression in one partner often brings out depressive symptoms in the other (Tower and Kasl, 1996). Either way, partners can be left feeling emotionally distanced and trapped in negative ways of relating to one another as closeness is lost (e.g. see Nelson and Beach, 1990; Schmaling and Jacobson, 1990). Sexual problems are also common (see d'Ardenne and Morrod, 2003).

"One day I will wake up and feel awful and the day goes awful and I shout at my partner more than I normally do and I find myself very aggressive and pent up and full of anger and I don't know what at... but another day I wake up feeling absolutely fine."

(Teresa, Dudley)

The links between depression and relationship problems are summarised in Figure 2.11.

Relationship challenges and processes
How depression erodes the couple relationship
Conflicting demands

A depressed partner can make conflicting, heavy demands on their partner. Because of their low self-esteem and negative outlook they can excessively seek reassurance. But a depressed partner also looks to a well partner to confirm the negative picture they have drawn of themselves. These confusing and conflicting demands become tiring and frustrating for the well partner (Joiner and Metalsky, 1995; Katz, 2001).

Trapped in negativity

A depressed partners' negative outlook on themselves, the world and their future can create a sense of hopelessness in the family. Depressed partners can also be very negative towards a partner. They are often critical and attacking and attempt to coerce a partner to change. Because non-depressed partners feel undermined and attacked by their partner they can become defensive or counterattacking. This is seen by the depressed individual as a lack of support and acceptance and is, in turn, met with defensiveness, counterattack and withdrawal (Gottman et al., 2002).

"He thought I was unhappy with him, and I thought I wasn't happy with him, and this made him unhappy with me, so it put a terrible strain on us both. Both of us thought it was a problem with our relationship, rather than what I was feeling."

(Mary, Huddersfield)

Key points:

- Couples coping with depression can get caught up in cycles of growing unhappiness in the relationship – apparent in communication problems and declining support – that exacerbate the depression.

- This in turn can create further communication problems and undermine the relationship through ongoing conflict, criticism and negativity.

Figure 2.11: Relationship difficulties and depression

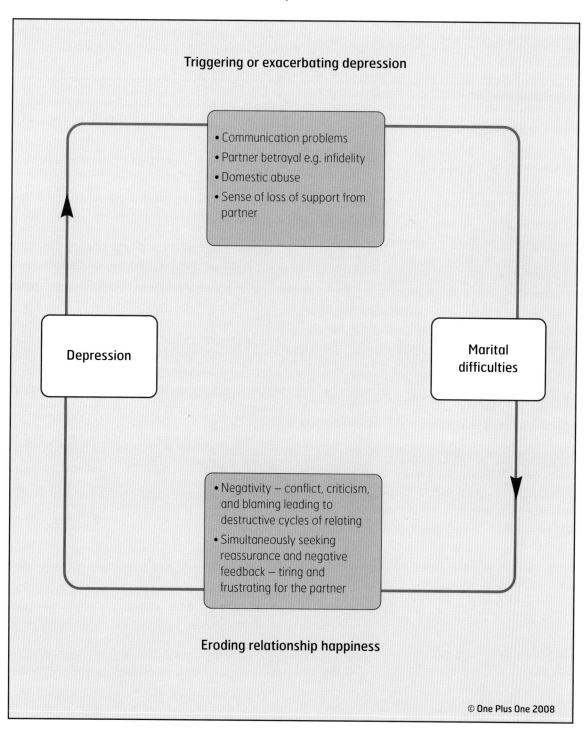

Triggering or exacerbating depression

- Communication problems
- Partner betrayal e.g. infidelity
- Domestic abuse
- Sense of loss of support from partner

Depression

Marital difficulties

- Negativity – conflict, criticism, and blaming leading to destructive cycles of relating
- Simultaneously seeking reassurance and negative feedback – tiring and frustrating for the partner

Eroding relationship happiness

How relationship problems trigger depression

Aspects of the marital relationship may also trigger depression or exacerbate it e.g. turning a depressive episode into chronic depression (Harris et al., 1999).

Poor communication

Communication difficulties and poor problem-solving skills can create stress in the relationship. Stress precipitates depression and partners then continue to struggle to communicate as they get trapped in a negative outlook which leaves them down about themselves and stuck in hurtful ways of relating to one another (Banawan et al., 2002). This couple managed to keep talking:

"I got Moira to own up to it. I said "I know how I feel, I feel low". I told her how I felt, and hoped that she would tell me how she felt – it was obvious she did, the symptoms were there. That would sometimes start good conversations. At least we acknowledged things."

(John, Brighton)

Emotional vulnerability

Depressed individuals are particularly sensitive to criticism, family tension and hostility. This is not only the case during a depressive bout but also when a partner is recovering from a depressive episode. Relationship problems can therefore trigger a relapse. One study found that the best predictor of a female partner's depressive relapse was their answer to the question 'How critical is your partner of you?' (Hooley and Teasdale, 1989).

Loss of support

Support is important to a relationship. If a partner feels unsupported they are more likely to develop depression because the lack of support threatens their sense of the partner as a secure base (Banawan et al., 2002). If a relationship is in the process of breaking down, it is not uncommon for one or both partners to become depressed.

Depression in the postnatal period

Between 10 per cent to 15 per cent of women are affected by postnatal depression. Relationship difficulties often coexist with postnatal depression, although the cause and effect between them is not fully understood (Murray and Cooper, 1997). Coping with it can be particularly hard given all the other adjustments that couples face at that time.

"...all Paul has to do is to come in and say the wrong thing and I start fighting myself and fighting him and I just feel so pent up. One night Paul is coming home to a wife who is alright, full of beans and another night he comes home and I'm walking around screaming and crying my eyes out."

(Shenaz, Southampton)

Mothers are more likely to develop postnatal depression if a father is not as supportive as she had expected (Cox et al., 1999; Cowan and Cowan, 2000). This may be experienced either as a lack of support or as over-controlling behaviour.

Although couples coping with depression in the postnatal period will face the same kinds of challenges as couples coping with depression at other times, the link between relationship problems and depression may be even stronger and more lasting (O'Hara et al., 1990). Postnatal depression is also likely to have a particularly negative impact on women's sexual satisfaction (Larsen and O'Hara, 2002).

Men living with a postnatally depressed partner are more likely to experience depression and emotional difficulties, such as anxiety and mood disorders, during the postnatal period. For example, one study found that 50 per cent of fathers whose wives were suffering from postnatal depression were also experiencing depression (Ballard and Davies, 1996). Overall, USA data suggest that between 10 per cent to 15 per cent of fathers experience depression during the postpartum period (Raskin et al., 1990). This new father struggled with his partner's postnatal depression:

"That was the worst year of my life, when it should have been the best. Although I never told my wife, I wished we'd never thought about the idea of having a baby. I feel differently now but at the time it felt like it had ruined my life."

(Frank, Chester)

Unmarried adolescent fathers are particularly vulnerable to depression, guilt and anxiety (see Spector, 2006). But depression in fathers is often masked by excessive drinking, overwork or obsessive involvement in hobbies.

Which relationships are most vulnerable?

Risk factors include:

- **Pre-existing stress** – Couples who are already living in challenging circumstances are more vulnerable to depression and its impact on their relationship.

- **Humiliation in the relationship** – Women who feel humiliated in their relationship, for example, because a partner has been unfaithful, are at greater risk of depression than women whose relationships break down for other reasons. Similarly, in violent relationships, the humiliating and controlling tactics that often accompany the violence are linked to the development of depression (Banawan et al., 2002).

- **Gender** – Women are twice as likely as men to experience clinical depression and are more vulnerable to developing depression as a result of relationship problems than men (Whisman, 2001; Fincham et al., 1997). However, men are more likely to become depressed following a divorce or separation than women (Bruce and Kim, 1992).

Couple relationships and alcohol abuse

- Alcoholic men are four times more likely to be physically violent than a non-alcoholic partner (O'Farrel and Murphy, 1995; Murphy and O'Farrel, 1997).

- Three-quarters of couples seeking relationship counselling in a study reported fighting often over how much a partner was drinking (Halford et al, 1993).

Relationships where one or both partners are problem drinkers come under great stress. They are vulnerable to conflict, distress, violence and breakdown (e.g. see Floyd, 2006). Relationship difficulties can also be a trigger for drinking, or perpetuate alcohol abuse; an argument with a partner often precedes a drinking bout. Relationship problems invariably result in relapse for alcoholics (Hore, 1971).

Relationship challenges and processes

Poor communication and negative feelings

Couples dealing with alcoholism often get stuck in unsupportive and destructive ways of communicating with one another (Jacob et al., 1981). The alcoholic partner tends to be negative, defensive and often aggressive, particularly when they are under the influence of alcohol (Weinberg and Vogler, 1990). In many cases, communication problems and conflict suppress the good things in the relationship – warmth, affection and support – and leave the relationship overwhelmed by criticism, conflict and withdrawal (Floyd et al., 2006).

Managing the stigma of a substance abusing partner

Partners often try and keep their partner's alcoholism secret because they feel ashamed of what is happening and want to protect the alcoholic partner and children. This puts enormous pressure on the well partner. He or she can feel angry at being put in such a position and isolated from friends and family.

Sexual problems

Sexual problems are common in alcohol abusing partnerships: they may be a direct result of the effects of alcoholism on physiological functioning; reflect partners' unhappiness in the relationship e.g. poor communication and lack of support; or reflect feelings towards a partner when he is drunk (O'Farrel and Choquette, 1991).

Escalating aggression and violence

Escalating aggression and violence are all too frequent in relationships where one partner is an alcoholic. Because alcohol acts as a disinhibitor, it increases aggression.

"He lost his job and he started drinking, and then he got quite violent."

(Ros, Bristol)

In general, alcoholic partners are also less confident in their ability to weather conflicts without drinking, which means that arguments often coincide with drinking sessions. As alcoholics

can find it difficult to back down from an argument, conflict can easily escalate into violence. Alcoholic men are four times more likely to be physically violent than a non-alcoholic partner (O'Farrel and Murphy, 1995; Murphy and O'Farrel, 1997).

Problematic personal attributes

Some of these relationship difficulties are related to the traits of the alcoholic partner. Alcoholics are more likely to have aggressive personality traits and suffer from problems in their thinking abilities (Dolan and Nathan, 2002).

Which relationships are most vulnerable?

Some relationships are more vulnerable to the impact of alcohol abuse than others. Issues include:

Complicating factors – Alcoholics are often struggling with other substance abuse issues, such as drugs. They are also more prone to other psychological disorders, such as depression (Nolan et al., 2001). Both factors will impose additional pressure on the relationship, as in the case of Nadine:

"Well, though I may think 'Oh, it was easier then' it was actually quite difficult as well. Paul had had

Key points:

- Couples where one or both partners abuse alcohol often fall into negative cycles of relating.
- Challenges to the relationship include: communication problems; stigma and the isolation associated with hiding the abuse from those outside of the family; the loss of positive ways of relating and escalating conflict and the risk of violence.

clinical depression and had been self-harming and he also had a drink problem, so our relationship had been tough. I had borne the brunt of this – I was there, and stuck by him. It had been tough actually."

(Nadine, London)

The male is an alcoholic – Relationships where the alcoholic partner is male tend to do worse than where the female partner is abusing alcohol. This is because alcoholic men tend to blame circumstances or other people for their drinking problem. Alcoholic women tend to accept responsibility for their drinking and its effect on their relationship (Noel et al., 1991).

Binge drinking – Binge drinking is generally more harmful to a relationship than steady drinking. 'Steady' drinkers are more likely to drink at home, whereas binge drinkers can be gone for periods of time (Dolan and Nathan, 2002). Couples are also more likely to argue if one partner is a heavy drinker (Floyd et al., 2006).

Economic pressures and work stress

- Approximately a fifth of the population lived below the poverty line in 2004/2005 (www.poverty.org.uk).
- Work-stress and lack of work-life balance is the third most common reason why couples seek Relate counselling (Relate, 2008).

Economic and work pressures can take their toll on the couple relationship. Whether partners have too much work or no work the stress associated with their situation can affect how they get on.

Relationship challenges and processes
Stress and depression
Economic stress affects the relationship indirectly because of its impact on partners' depression and psychological well-being. If couples get through it, it can bring them closer together:

"When Said was depressed about work I saw a different side to him and realised how it influences his life. So I feel I know him better now and I'm closer to him."

(Sharon, Derby)

As the previous section demonstrates, partners coping with depression can become withdrawn, see their partners in a negative light, and are more prone to conflict and destructive ways of relating. Partners caught in these cycles do not provide each other with the support they need and they can spiral into further distress and conflict (see Conger et al., 1990; Vinokur et al., 1996). Ian and Kate became trapped in conflict, which began to trouble the children:

"...we had serious money problems. It was a tough time and if I'm honest neither of us handled it well.... we kept blaming each other. We didn't want the children to worry, we didn't tell them anything... our son asked if we were splitting up. We sat down with the children and gave them the simple facts, that money was tight which meant we had to work harder and as we got tired we got grumpy. I think it reassured them that we were going to sort it out. It was a relief to share it as a family."

(Kate, Harrogate)

Key point:
- Economic stress puts pressure on the couple relationship because of its impact on partners' mental health.

Figure 2.12: Economic strain and relationship difficulties

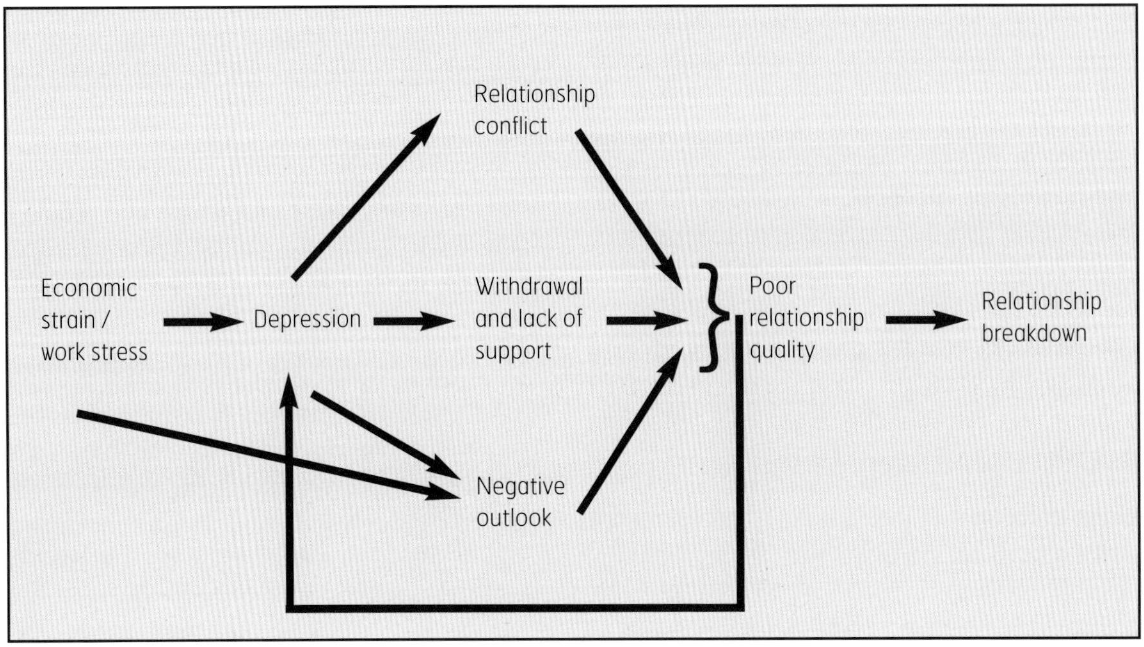

Thinking the worst

Stress can also have a direct impact on our thought processes. Partners under stress can find it difficult to take a positive view of each other and the motives underlying their behaviour. Which means that couples under stress tend to see their partners in a negative light. And this gets increasingly difficult as other aspects of life are seen to be going badly (Tesser and Beach, 1998; Neff and Karney, 2004).

"When I look back we did used to row more, probably just the stress of the money side of things. It was all a burden for me. He was oblivious and just, I had to get on with it and he was unaware."

(Naomi, Lincoln)

It can also depend on pre-existing levels of stress and anxiety. Research suggests that couples can recognise and accommodate negative events up

to a certain point. Beyond that point relationship happiness plummets. For example, one study found that women who were already experiencing high levels of stress were more likely to experience a drop in relationship satisfaction when they encountered additional difficulties (Karney et al., 2003). This means that families in already challenging circumstances start off more vulnerable to the impact of economic and work stress.

Still caring

Couples who cope with these stressful circumstances manage to maintain a level of empathy for their partner. They are concerned about them and caring and helpful even as they deal with their own worries. Couples also do better when they have good communication skills and can manage their differences in a way that does not undermine the relationship (Conger et al., 2002).

For example, this woman managed to remain concerned about the impact of work on her partner:

"All my husband did was go to work and decorate the house. He had no input in the early years of my children. But he needed to – we needed the money. My husband has worked extremely hard career-wise. He has always done overtime, because he had to. During the eighties, he earned just enough to keep our heads above water. He used to work 13 hours a day, then he would come home, have his dinner and go to sleep. We had no adult life at all in terms of socialising. And he had nearly no days off – he would work 13 days on the trot. Then on his one day off he did the garden."

(Margaret, Eastbourne)

Work stress

Relationships can also suffer when one or both partners are under pressure at work. The stress associated with work affects couples in the same way as economic pressures arising out of worklessness; it affects partners' mental health. Its impact is not confined to the working partner as difficulties can affect both partners (Matthews et al., 1996). It also has an impact on day-to-day mood so that a stressed partner can come home irritable, fed up, anxious or angry (Matthews et al., 1996), as in the case of this couple:

"He would come home from work and he'd be really narked off because his job was getting on his nerves and he'd take it out on me. And I'd say 'oh for Christ's sake leave your job and get another job then' or something you know and it just got a bit..."

(Emma, Truro)

Some researchers suggest that these day-to-day responses are influenced by gender. Women's moods are more affected by their workday

experience. Men are more likely to compartmentalise their work experiences and become more withdrawn (Schulz et al., 2004). This father was able to recognise how these patterns can be damaging:

"I would walk in and I would be knackered, but I'd have to remember that they had their issues still, and Lisa may have had a really difficult day, and she would have been with the children all day. That's a different kind of tired – it's full on, dedicated to another person, always on your guard. I would have to remember that."

(Hugh, London)

Which relationships are most vulnerable?

Couples who are already living in challenging circumstances are more vulnerable to the impact of economic stress on their relationship (Tesser and Beach, 1998).

Infidelity

How common are affairs?

- 'Adultery' is cited in approximately one fifth of divorces as the reason for the break down of the marriage (National Statistics, 2008a).
- Affairs were the most common reason for seeking help from Relate in 2008 (Relate, 2008).

Given their secretive nature, and the continuing social disapproval attached to them, it is difficult to obtain reliable estimates of the proportion of relationships affected by infidelity. Estimates range from 10 per cent to 40 per cent (Johnson et al., 2001; Gordon et al., 2004; Hall and Fincham, 2005). In a national survey of marital therapists, extramarital affairs were ranked as the second most damaging problem to relationships, with only physical abuse having a more negative impact (Whisman et al., 1997).

Reasons underlying affairs

However, infidelity is not necessarily the cause of a relationship breakdown. People have affairs for a number of reasons:

- for people frightened of commitment or intimacy, an affair stops them getting too close to their partner or becoming dependent on the relationship. This often reflects painful past experiences;
- for some, an affair might offer the excitement of 'forbidden fruit'; and
- an affair might reflect pre-existing weaknesses and signify the need to renegotiate or end the primary relationship (Colman, 1995; Hall and Fincham, 2005). This is more likely to be the case if a female partner is involved in an affair.

In general, men tend to become involved in purely sexual affairs and the affair is often unrelated to how satisfied they are in the relationship. Women's affairs are generally more emotionally charged and the affair a reflection of unhappiness with the primary relationship (see Hall and Fincham, 2005).

Different types of affairs

The reasons underlying the affair will also be linked to the type of affair in which a partner has been involved. Affairs differ:

- an affair could involve emotional unfaithfulness – when a partner channels their emotional energy into another relationship – but there is no sexual consummation;
- an affair may be largely sexual with no emotional investment; and
- or an affair may combine sexual and emotional intimacy. A relationship is least likely to recover from sexual and emotional unfaithfulness, although the chances are better if a partner confesses to the affair rather than being discovered (Hall and Fincham, 2005).

Key points:

- The impact of infidelity on the 'betrayed' partner is similar to the trauma induced by physical or sexual abuse.
- Many couples separate following an affair. Those that remain together have to work through a series of stages that gives the betrayed partner time to process the emotional impact; understand what has happened and why; and work together to re-negotiate and re-establish the relationship.

Relationship challenges and processes

Emotional trauma

A partner's experience of infidelity has been likened to the posttraumatic stress reactions of victims of emotional, physical and sexual abuse. Because infidelity undermines the shared identity and 'protected space' of a close relationship, infidelity can leave the betrayed partner feeling violated (Afifi et al., 2001). It can also undermine a partner's sense of the future – all that they trusted in and expected – and leave him or her feeling like they have lost control over the direction of their life.

"It's been eight years now since the affair and it's only just this last, maybe I'd say two years, that it doesn't bother me. I can sit here and talk about it."

(Ali, Barnsley)

When an affair is discovered, or revealed, the hurt partner is likely to feel intense pain, shame, fear of abandonment, guilt, disillusionment, and rage. They are likely to find it hard to stop thinking about it, have nightmares, and experience flashbacks. Depression, anxiety and self-blame are also likely (Silverstein, 1998). The experience can feel like riding an emotional roller coaster (Olson et al., 2002).

The impact of infidelity can vary according to the type of affair. Sexual unfaithfulness is more likely to leave a partner angry and shocked. Emotional unfaithfulness has a greater impact on a partner's sense of security and emotional well-being (Hall and Fincham, 2005). The impact is also likely to vary depending on which partner had an affair. Men are less likely to forgive a wife's affair and more likely to see it as the end of the marriage (Harrison and Allan, 2001).

Pathways for negotiating affairs

In an in-depth study of affairs couples described dealing with the fallout of an affair in different ways (Harrrison and Allan, 2001). These different 'pathways' are outlined in Figure 2.13.

Figure 2.13: Pathways for negotiating affairs

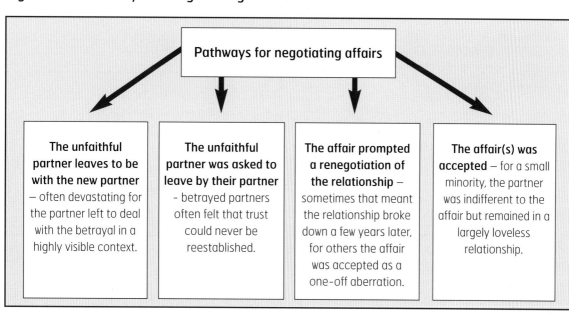

Recovering from an affair

Stages of recovery

Most couples have to navigate a number of different stages if they want to rebuild the relationship following infidelity (Gordon et al., 2004).

- The first stage involves processing and absorbing the impact of the trauma and normalising their experiences.

- The second stage requires understanding why the affair happened and what it means for the relationship.

- The third stage involves exploring forgiveness, renegotiating the relationship and establishing a new set of underlying beliefs and values for it.

Jackie accepted her partner back after he left for another woman two years previously. She feels their relationship has been strengthened:

"Since he has been back, we are a lot stronger. He is grateful that I did take him back – the sod! A lot of close friends knew that he had mistreated me. When I say that, I don't mean he beat me or anything but he hadn't given me any love or attention for ages. When he wanted to come back, he was very sorry. He told me 'I have always loved you, I just forgot how."

(Jackie, Newcastle)

Getting stuck

If couples do not resolve their experience of infidelity they can remain stuck in the past. For example, the hurt partner is unable to trust the unfaithful partner and cannot take the risks needed in order to move on. If the relationship breaks down, partners are likely to carry unresolved hurts into subsequent relationships (Gordon et al., 2004).

Managing the strong feelings

As couples try and work through the impact of an affair feelings often run high. The hurt partner usually needs to be able to express how the affair has impacted them. But it is challenging for couples to manage the anger and negativity that needs to be expressed and they can struggle to find ways to do it without getting caught up in embittered exchanges. Partners are also likely to process an affair at different rates. The unfaithful partner generally wants to move on and put the affair behind them. But the hurt partner is likely to continue to feel the intensity of the trauma and a need to understand why the affair happened (Gordon et al., 2004).

Which relationships are most vulnerable?

Relationships are more vulnerable to infidelity when circumstances provide a partner with the opportunity to be unfaithful, for example, when they are working away from home. Not surprisingly, an affair is more likely to happen when one or both partners are unhappy in the relationship.

Sexual difficulties

- Sexual problems are one of the most common reasons why people seek counselling from Relate.
- According to the Lancet in 2001 most heterosexual adults between the ages of 16 and 44 have sex on average 1.5 times a week (Johnson et al., 2001).

Sexual difficulties are common (Relate, 2008). But as with many of the other issues in this section, they can be a symptom of or a cause of relationship difficulties. For example, a sexual problem, such as premature ejaculation puts pressure on the relationship. The same is true of other common physical problems, such as loss of libido, impaired ejaculation, and inability to climax. Very often, difficulties are caused by performance anxiety, which may be linked to a recent or past experience (such as losing an erection during sex), and which, in turn affect normal biological responses.

Sexual problems can also be a symptom of other difficulties in the relationship. For example, arguing about how often to have sex can really be an argument about feeling loved and cared for and partners' failure to meet each other's deeper needs for connection and affection. The loss of closeness makes sex out of the question.

"He went one side of the bed, I went the other side. It was very, very sad indeed. It was awful. On the sexual side of things everything changed. We used to have a good sex life, but then things just became very mechanistic. I would make a joke of it but I went through all the emotions – you name it. It was just cold and even though we were in bed together I felt really lonely without him."

(Corrine, Lampeter)

Relationship challenges and processes
Changing needs over time
Sexual needs are caught up with emotional and physical needs. Life events and transitions affect partners' sexual desires and needs. Sex may become less important as couples deal with, for example, becoming parents, the different stage of the relationship, unemployment, changes in contraception, physical and mental ill-health, and ageing. Becky lost interest in sex after the baby arrived:

"The change in our sex life has been dramatic... I'm just not interested anymore. I'm tired, I want space, it's the last thing on my mind. I'm worried there's a danger of it becoming a pattern. I think he's finding it quite hard but we've talked about it, sometimes argued, but it seems alright."

(Becky, North Wales).

As most people experience many if not all of these events, most couples encounter sexual difficulties at some point in their relationship. Sexual problems are the most commonly cited reason for seeking counselling.

Libido and arousal
Interest in sex and frequency of sexual intercourse varies from person to person, and from women to men. Sex is generally more important to men. Sexual intimacy is often a way for men to express their love for their partner. And the closeness and loving contact it conveys is important to them.

"I think sex is an important part of a relationship, it makes me feel really close to my wife. Sometimes it is difficult to say stuff or we have had a row, but when we have sex we are more relaxed and able to talk about things more easily – although sometimes I fall asleep!!!"

(Oliver, Coventry)

> **Key points:**
> - Sexual problems are common at times of transition or stress.
> - Sexual problems might be putting the relationship under pressure, or couple difficulties might be the root of sexual problems.

For women, it is often more complex. They take longer to become aroused. And sexual intercourse is often the culmination of other expressions of love and affection, such as the partner taking some responsibility for the house, or meeting some of her emotional needs. When a woman feels tired and empty she can find little enthusiasm or desire for sexual intercourse. But this may mean her partner's means of expressing and experiencing love are shut down.

Communication

Couples often find it very difficult to communicate about sex.

"The first couple of years of marriage, I couldn't talk to my husband because he used to get so hurt... his male ego — I couldn't suggest anything."

(Sasha, Colchester)

Failure to communicate means that each others' needs, anxieties, fears and feelings are not heard or understood. Feelings affect behaviour, and finding a way to address feelings, and help them be understood, can help partners to address some of the problems around making love. Even if couples are not good with words, they can use non-verbal cues and other body movements to convey messages that might be more difficult to express verbally when they make love.

Myths and misunderstandings

Many simple sexual problems arise out of ignorance, feelings of guilt and anxiety, or false expectations and myths. Common media messages and myths about sex include:

- Sex should be natural and spontaneous — asking for it spoils it.
- Men always want and are ready for sex.
- Sex is for male pleasure — a woman's duty is to fill his need and not her own.
- Men must take charge of and orchestrate sex.
- If women aren't orgasmic they should fake it.
- Women expect men to know all about sex.
- Men should not have or express certain feelings such as vulnerability and tenderness.
- For men, in sex, as elsewhere, it is performance that counts.
- If the woman doesn't have an orgasm, the man has failed.
- Having sex means having intercourse.
- For the couple to have sex, the man must have an erection.
- Good sex always ends in orgasm.
- A woman ought to have orgasms during intercourse, other means don't count.
- There is something wrong with a man who has a lower sex drive than a woman.
- In general, women receive more stimulation from a large penis than a small one.
- You shouldn't make love to a woman when she's pregnant or having her period.

> ### Box 2.4. Supporting couples experiencing sexual problems
>
> Part three outlines tools to use in supporting couples with relationship difficulties. As you get them to tell their story, useful points to understand and clarify include:
>
> - What might be going on in bed that could be affecting their relationship?
> - What might be going on in their lives that could lead to problems with sex?
> - What aspects of their past, such as the relationship history, their individual sexual histories and experiences, and their childhood experiences, might be affecting sexual intimacy?
>
> Appendix 6 contains some ideas on supporting couples who are experiencing sexual problems.

Which relationships are most at risk?

Relationships are more vulnerable to sexual problems (that do not have a physical cause) when partners struggle to cope with the pressures on the relationship that occur during times of transition and stress.

Verbal and physical aggression

The focus of this publication is on responding to everyday relationship problems that clients raise.

- 1 in 4 women experience domestic abuse over their lifetimes.
- Domestic violence accounts for between 16 per cent and 25 per cent of all recorded violent crime.

(Women's Aid, 2008)

Domestic abuse is not an everyday issue but an unacceptable physical, emotional, sexual, or financial abuse of a partner. But it is a common occurrence. Research suggests that one in four women experience domestic violence over their lifetimes and between six and ten per cent of women suffer domestic violence in a given year (Council of Europe, 2002). A survey of Relate Centres found that domestic violence was mentioned in 1 in 5 of their sessions on the day of the survey (Stanko, 2000). The vast majority of abuse is perpetrated against women (Johnson and Ferraro, 2000).

Pregnant women or those with young families are the most vulnerable to partner aggression (CPHVA, 2005). But it is not confined to any social class or setting.

"In the nine weeks we knew her this was the first time we knew about it. If I ever needed reminding that domestic violence knows no boundaries, she did it for me. Can you imagine that — just leaving your country with your son and a suitcase?"

(Children's Centre worker)

Domestic violence is generally understood as an attempt to control, dominate or gain power over the partner. Violent and non-violent tactics of control are utilised, including emotional abuse (see Johnson and Ferraro (2000) for a discussion about different kinds of violence). Women's Aid (2008) argue strongly that couple based support, such as counselling, is not an appropriate response to domestic violence. If a woman discloses her experiences during a counselling session with her partner she is at risk of further abuse as a result of reprisal against her disclosure. Fear, and her partner's denial, also mean a woman is unlikely to express her true feelings and the true extent of the abuse if she is in a joint session with her partner.

Responding to a disclosure of domestic violence

This section does not attempt to provide an in-depth account of abuse within couple relationships. What is offered here is a pointer to other sources of help as well as some brief guidance. It is by no means comprehensive. One source of guidance will be the local inter-agency domestic violence forum. There are 200 across the country. The national Women's Aid office, the local council (via their contact person for the domestic violence forum) or local police domestic violence unit should have details.

Key point:
- Women who are ready to disclose abuse need to know they will be listened to, supported, and believed.

Part three of this publication sets out essential skills for working with clients with relationship difficulties. The skills are also invaluable in supporting women (and most victims are women) as they disclose partner abuse, but the way that disclosure is followed up is vital. Local procedures must be followed in order to ensure all parties are protected and information gathered safely and appropriately (Good practice guidance on responding to domestic abuse is provided in Appendix 7).

It is also important to be alert to indicators of domestic abuse. Victims of domestic violence have said repeatedly that they would be willing and relieved to disclose the violence if they thought that those they spoke to e.g. the nurse, midwife, or health visitor were likely to be empathetic and emotionally supportive. Being listened to and believed are a crucial first step in the recovery process.

Leaving a violent relationship

It is also helpful to remember that leaving a violent relationship is a process, not a one-off act. Some women will never leave. Neither is leaving without its risks. The period during which a woman is planning or making her exit is often the most dangerous time for her and her children. It is not uncommon for perpetrators to threaten to harm or even kill their partners or children if she leaves.

Other reasons may also be important, such as: fear of isolation; uncertainty about where to go; worries about money; and exhaustion and depression (Women's Aid, 2008). Anne did not know what changed for her when she decided to leave:

"I was fed up with being pushed around I think, and I just thought to myself 'No, I've had enough, this is it. I'm 35 years old, I've been pushed around since I was 17, I don't think I could have taken no more you know and that was it. I just thought that's it. I've had enough. And I don't know where it comes from, and to this day I still don't know but I done it."

(Anne, Woking)

A client may feel in a stronger position if she receives support to think through her and her children's personal safety and to make plans for what she will do in a crisis. If she is contemplating leaving the client needs to know that:

- she and her children will be taken seriously;
- that their rights will be enforced; and
- she will have access to the financial and practical resources she needs.

If a woman is not sure that the support she needs is there she may not feel able to leave (Women's Aid, 2008).

Box 2.5: Practitioner resources on domestic violence

- CPHVA Clinical effectiveness bulletin 18c **www.amicustheunion.org/cphva/pdf/Bulletin18c.pdf**. This offers a list of sources of professional guidance and other information.
- CPHVA – **www.amicus-cphva.org** Professional Briefing - Domestic violence: A framework of good practice **www.msfcphva.org/members/professbriefings/prbdovi.pdf**
- Royal College of Nursing – Domestic Violence: Guidance for Nurses **www.rcn.org.uk**
- Responding to domestic abuse: a handbook for health professionals (Department of Health, 2005).

Which relationships are most at risk?

Factors associated with increased risk of domestic violence include poverty (though not social class) and youth: women under the age of 30 are at considerably greater risk than those over the age of 40 years (Women's Aid, 2008).

Key Messages

- Although relationships face different challenges the impact is often similar. Pressures can lead to depression and affect partners' ability to communicate and offer support to one another. As a result, couples can get stuck in destructive cycles of relating.

- Individual coping strategies affect how resilient the relationship is to the pressures it is under. Couples can struggle when they have different coping techniques, especially when the coping techniques are unhelpful, such as being overprotective. Couples are likely to manage best when they adopt a problem solving approach that helps them to find practical solutions to their difficulties.

- Many couples struggle to protect their sexual relationship when they experience stressful life events such as ill-health, depression, becoming parents, and partner infidelity. Couples benefit from sensitive help to articulate their needs and find ways to meet them.

- Couples are often most vulnerable to the impact of external pressures when they are already coping with circumstances which deplete their resilience, such as financial hardship, depression or ill-health. Or when they have limited personal resources, such as poor communication skills or problematic personality traits.

4. When things go wrong

This section explores what happens when relationships break down and the support that parents and children are most likely to find helpful when they are facing relationship difficulties.

The stages of relationship breakdown

As the section on conflict illustrates, relationship breakdown often follows a predictable course. As Figure 2.14 shows, partners often get stuck in patterns of poor communication, lose closeness and intimacy, and begin to avoid or refuse to have sex. Finally, couples drift apart and become detached – often over a number of years.

Figure 2.14: The ending of a relationship

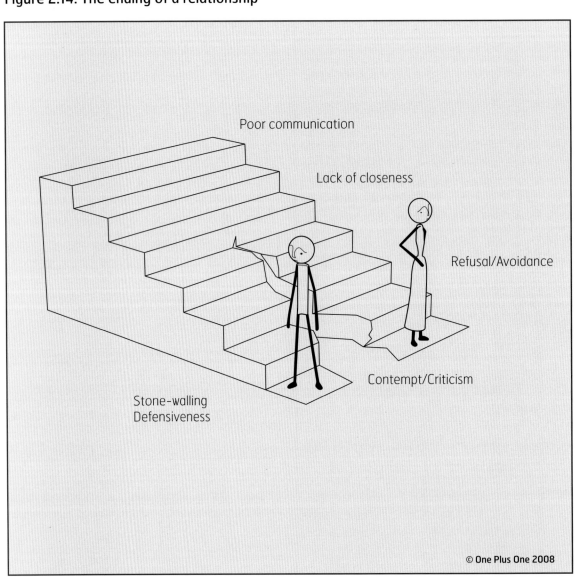

Poor communication

Lack of closeness

Refusal/Avoidance

Contempt/Criticism

Stone-walling
Defensiveness

© One Plus One 2008

Although all relationships vary, researchers have mapped out the stages that many relationships go through as they break down (e.g. see Kayser and Rao, 2005; Rollie and Duck, 2005). Partners' behaviour is often similar to the stages an infant goes through when it is separated from its attachment figure: protest and anger; cling and seek; despair and depression; detachment and separation. However, partners do not necessarily move through these phases at the same time. It can be a shock to one partner to find out that the other one has been contemplating the end of the relationship.

Protest and anger

Couples in the early stages of difficulties are often caught up in conflict and anger. These feelings usually represent an attempt to re-engage with a partner and are an expression of deep-seated fears that they will lose their secure base – their partner – should the relationship end.

Cling and seek

As difficulties continue partners desperately seek to get through to each other and to re-engage. This may be more characteristic of women, as accounts of relationship breakdown have found that women often respond to problems in these early phases by trying to please their partners. They often feel responsible for the relationship and go to great lengths to take care of the partner and the partnership (Kayser and Rao, 2005).

Despair and depression

In contrast to those clinging on to a relationship, some individuals may appear to have lost hope. They may have had a period of depression a few years previously and have been left with few positive feelings about the relationship, or may even be thinking about leaving. At the same time,

the other partner may be desperately clinging to the relationship.

Apathy, indifference and detachment

Detachment often follows depression and when a couple reaches the later stages of relationship breakdown one or both partners will be disengaged. In these final stages, the strong feelings of anger and hurt have often been replaced by apathy and indifference.

"I don't bother any more. I just let it run its course. Even though it's running down hill."

(Phil, Loughborough)

Some partners will start to take steps to end the relationship. One or both partners may have an affair, which is usually a symptom of a dying relationship, not the cause.

Figure 2.15. The stages of relationship breakdown relationship

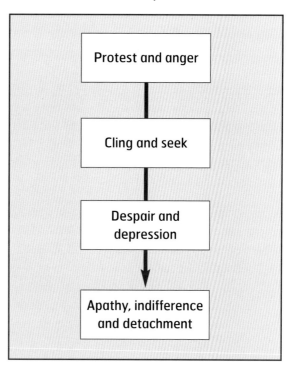

Endings

When a relationship is in its last stages couples are likely to:

- see their marital problems as severe;
- fail to see the point of talking things over. They have usually resorted to solving difficulties independently of each other;
- lead parallel lives; and
- feel lonely in the relationship.

(Source: Gottman, 1994b)

In general, men and women have different ways of ending relationships. Men are more likely to end a relationship by avoiding interaction, or changing the subject when a partner mentions problems or seeks to talk about the future of the relationship. Women, on the other hand, are more likely to tell a partner that a relationship is over or to explain why they are unhappy with it (Duck and Wood, 2005).

Partners in these later stages have usually rewritten their relationship histories. They remember the low points, such as a partner's failings, unhappy holidays or even disappointments with the wedding day. The negativity in the relationship not only overpowers the present but it also overwhelms partners' memories of the past. Children can find this very distressing as it also rewrites their childhood experiences and leaves them wondering what was true.

At this point, problems often move from being a private issue to being publicly aired. Women are generally more likely than men to start talking to their friends about what is going on and to seek their support (Rubin, 1985). A couple may also seek counselling, but it is usually too late as one or both partners have disengaged from the relationship.

"If they present too late relationship counselling may not help because they are in the first stage of separation and do not want to learn about one another."

(Counsellor)

For many individuals, counselling is as much about help with leaving the relationship, or a way of ensuring the other partner is cared for, as a last ditch attempt to save the relationship (Kayser and Rao, 2005). Partners will often also start talking to those around them about what is going on in the relationship. Despite indifference, one or both partners may focus on the other's flaws as they mentally prepare their personal accounts for leaving and try and get listeners to agree with their own, rewritten account of the relationship (Rollie and Duck, 2005).

Supporting families when things go wrong

Children invariably get caught in the crossfire of problems between parents. The next section highlights some of the ways that an informed and sensitive practitioner can support families when parents' relationships are in trouble. More in-depth publications are available (see Appendices). You may also want to access One Plus One's training for working with parents in conflict *My Mum and Dad Argue a Lot* (see Appendix 2). Practitioners have found the course gives them the confidence to tackle these issues:

"It has helped with my confidence. Talking about conflict can be difficult. You're aware that you are tackling very sensitive subjects. Somebody may be talking about the fact that they are thinking about whether staying in a relationship is worth it or not, and that can be quite scary to deal with as you don't want to say or do the wrong thing..."

(Parenting Facilitator)

Children and parental relationship problems

Our understanding of the impact of parental relationship difficulties on children is subject to a host of myths and misunderstandings. Contrary to popular belief:

- girls are as vulnerable to the adverse impact of separation as boys;

- adolescents can be as troubled by relationship breakdown as young children; and

- the impact of divorce or separation is not always immediately apparent but can emerge much later, with children appearing 'unscathed' for some time afterwards.

Perhaps most importantly, research challenges the myth that parental separation or divorce is an event. Rather, it highlights the extent to which separation or divorce are part of a process that begins long before the actual departure of one parent and continues throughout childhood. And how parents get on after separation is as important as how parents get on when they are together (Rodgers and Pryor, 1998).

Children and parental conflict

Children's experience of parental conflict is one of the factors that influences how they respond to parental relationship problems[6]. The accepted wisdom for many years around parental conflict was 'don't argue in front of the children'. But how parents manage disagreements is much more important than where or how often they argue.

Children can be affected by conflict in both positive and negative ways, depending on how parents handle it. Trying to keep conflict hidden generally creates anxiety; children pick up on problems between parents even if they have not seen them argue (see Reynolds, 2001).

"There have been times when our children spoke to us. I remember one time I was arguing with Fi about something or other, and we had really locked horns, or so I thought. But then later, my son stayed behind in the car to talk to me. He said: "Daddy, why were you shouting at mummy?" I didn't think I was shouting – I thought we were both shouting, and we were both batting it back and stuff – you know what I mean? But then he said "Well, I thought mummy was going to cry". So I listened, and then he said "I don't want you to do that again", so I said to him "OK". Basically, he had picked up on his mummy's energy where I hadn't. She was low and I hadn't recognised that. So I listened to him."

(Nick, Sunderland)

6. The evidence on children and conflict is based on an international review of studies on the subject (see Reynolds, 2001).

Box 2.6: Parental conflict and children

Destructive conflict – harmful and unresolved
Destructive conflict is particularly harmful to children. This type of conflict is characterised by verbal or physical aggression, non-verbal conflict or the 'silent' treatment, intense quarrelling, and arguments that are about or involve the children.

Productive conflict – unresolved but children may still learn from it
Productive conflict means that disputes are partially resolved or one parent changes the subject or gives in so that the argument does not continue. Children can learn from observing some of the ways parents handle conflict productively and are less harmed by it than destructive conflict.

"I don't like my mum and dad shouting but I do like it when it's over. They have a cuddle and get nice again."

(Matthew, Leeds)

Creative conflict – resolved and a good model for children to learn from
Children are least troubled by arguments where they see their parents apologise, negotiate, reach a compromise and resolve the argument. Observing parents handle difference well also helps children to acquire these important skills, such as humour and negotiation, for their own lives. Knowing that things are ok between their parents also means that children are more likely to feel secure and reassured. These parents have developed their own ways of letting the children know that everything is ok between them.

"When a fight starts you lose a bit of self control and you only think of yourselves. You forget the kids, get caught up in what you feel or in reacting to your partner. Then when it's all passed you just feel exhausted or relieved and forget the children haven't had that experience. I think you have to recognise what they've seen and heard. I say something they understand like 'Daddy was a pooh head but mummy's forgiven him!' Treating it like that gets everyone laughing. Even him!"

(Susie, Godalming)

The impact of couple relationship problems on children's well-being

Children who are exposed to destructive conflict express their distress in different ways.

- **A troublesome child** – Some children develop behavioural problems and become aggressive and difficult. This can put even more strain on parents as they struggle to cope and the behaviour can become a source of further conflict.

- **A sad and troubled child** – Some children develop emotional problems, such as anxiety and depression. When parents are preoccupied with problems in their relationship it is easy to overlook a child who is signalling her distress through quiet, withdrawn behaviour.

- **A parent child** – Other children deal with parental conflict by trying to comfort a parent or by trying to sort out the problem. This child-to-parent role reversal puts a child at risk of developing emotional and behavioural problems and of experiencing difficulties establishing healthy relationships in later life. Girls are particularly prone to responding in this way.

You can hear children talking about their experiences of parental conflict on One Plus One's interactive website – **www.thecoupleconnection.net.**

And when parents separate...

Children whose parents separate are also likely to respond in these ways as they struggle to deal with their feelings following their parents' separation (Pryor and Rodgers, 2001). Children are likely to do worse if parents continue to argue, even if the conflict is subtle and involves, for example, putting a former partner down in front of the children (Adamsons and Pasley, 2005). However, after approximately two years, most children settle back into a normal pattern of development (Pryor and Rodgers, 2001). And children who were in very discordant homes may actually do better if their parents separate and learn to manage their differences (Amato, 2000). If, however, parents who have separated continue to be engaged in embittered conflict, children continue to be at risk (Adamsons and Pasley, 2005). For a small minority of children, the impact of parental relationship problems resonates into adult life. Some children grow up to experience problems with alcohol use, in forming and maintaining relationships, in poorer life outcomes, such as poor employment prospects and in poorer health, including a tendency towards depression (Pryor and Rodgers, 2001).

What helps?

'Mediators and Moderators'

Part 1 of this publication explains some of the processes underlying the link between parents' relationship difficulties and children's well-being. The key question, though, is what helps? We know that children vary in their responses. Coping is related to:

- **children's characteristics** – including age, sex, temperament, and coping strategies;
- **the history of conflict in the family** – children become more sensitive to the impact of conflict the more they are exposed to it;
- **family circumstances** – the impact is likely to be greater if the family are coping with other stressful circumstances or events, such as parental depression, work stress or financial difficulties; and
- **previous experiences** – parental separation can also be particularly difficult for children who then go through, or have been through, more than one set of changes in family circumstances – multiple transitions – such as becoming part of a step-family (Pryor and Rodgers, 2001).

The following section summarises some of what we know about what helps.

Being reassured they are not to blame

In some families children become the scapegoat for their parents' problems. This is particularly harmful for children. But even where this does not happen, children often need to be reassured that they are not to blame for their parents' difficulties.

Sensitive understanding

When parents' relationships are in trouble, children can be helped by people who offer them genuine understanding, reassurance and practical support. If parents are separating, children need the opportunity to talk about their feelings, know they have been understood and ask questions. As is the case for adults, just 'being listened to' can be helpful.

Parents might find it helpful to understand the range of feelings that some children will experience.

Children often feel a great sense of loss and letting them grieve is an important part of helping them to deal with the situation and to move on to accept the changes in their family relationships. As they grieve they may go through a period of denial. They may also feel deeply angry towards their parents. Coping with these feelings can be hard for parents, especially if they feel they are to blame.

"Recently I've been working with a mum who has got a very angry daughter and daddy's not on the scene. Mum has got a new boyfriend, who's been around for four years, and the daughter resents him. Mum has been saying things like 'I don't know what is wrong with her'. I had to say 'I don't know your daughter, but I would suggest that part of it is about the fact that her dad is not around and she is hurting'. She said 'Oh no, I don't think that's the case at all'. But then she returned the following week and said 'Actually, maybe that's right'. It's a complex case – they have had CAMHS appointments and all of that – but the fact that the mum is beginning to acknowledge the effect of the relationship split is a big step."

(Children's Centre Worker)

People to talk to

Parents are often too distracted and distressed at the time of separation to appreciate their children's unhappiness or to provide the support they need. But support might be found through a sibling, friend, grandparent or other adult, such as a teacher or youth worker. Helplines, such as ChildLine, may also be useful. Knowing that they have help out there, even if they do not use it, can protect children against the impact of family stress (Kessler et al., 1996).

"If I had a problem, I think my teacher would be the first person I'd go to. 'Cos I wouldn't exactly like go to my dad and say 'Me, mum and my stepdad have been having an argument'. I'd prefer to go to my teacher, because I know my teacher wouldn't say anything."

(Terry, Lowestoft)

Being kept informed

Children benefit from being kept informed about what is happening in the family. If parents are caught up in conflict, children often worry that parents are about to split up. If parents have separated, children will have all sorts of worries about where they will live and what will happen to them. Children are helped if they can talk openly with both parents and parents can contain their differences (Hawthorne et al., 2003). Children also benefit from being involved in decisions about the future where age and circumstances make it appropriate (Dunn and Deater-Deckard, 2001).

Being kept out of it

Children are also hurt when they are forced into taking sides. Parents can help by not confiding inappropriately in their children and by keeping judgements about a partner to themselves.

"My dad left when I was 12. Things had been tense for quite a while and my mum said she was relieved that he had gone and so was I in a way. But it would start all over again when he rang up or visited. Afterwards she would burst into tears. I would make her a coffee and try to cheer her up but I would feel guilty. She said that if it wasn't for me she would not have to see him."

(Ceri, Hull)

Keeping in touch

Children invariably benefit from maintaining a relationship with the non-resident parent. And it may help to reassure them that a parent is still a parent even if he or she leaves the household to live somewhere else, as in the case of this mother:

"I did make a point of saying to them that he was still their dad and he's not changed in that respect. It's me he's fallen out with, not them."

(Mel, Stevenage)

Most children living in stepfamilies or with one parent still identify their biological father as their main father figure (Welsh et al., 2004). Fathers are more likely to stay engaged with their children if parents can get on and the mother encourages the father's involvement (Margolin et al., 2001).

Getting on together after relationship breakdown

Supporting children also means helping parents to manage their new, post-divorce relationship.

Working out 'the ending'

The first task for parents is to work out the story of the 'ending' of the relationship. As the section on the stages of relationship breakdown highlighted, separating partners usually need to tell their version of events. It is difficult to move on to a new phase if this does not happen. Being listened to and understood by a skilled practitioner can help parents to do this. If they are not given the 'mental space' to talk about the relationship parents will find it more difficult to think about the children and how they might be feeling. Children inevitably find this phase difficult as rewriting the relationship means that their childhoods can end up rewritten too.

From partner to co-parent

As parents 'work out the story' they also need to rethink the relationship with the parent and establish a new relationship – a co-parenting relationship – that is distinct from the romantic relationship they shared. In most cases it takes ex-partners around 2 years to find a new way of parenting together (Adamsons and Pasley, 2005).

Box 2.7: Tips for parents on communicating with a co-parent

- Avoid blaming yourself or your partner.
- Agree not to let your own relationship issues get into the discussion.
- Create some rules together about how best to manage meetings e.g. focusing on child-related issues.
- Continue at another time if you feel discussions sliding into tricky waters.
- Don't communicate with your partner through your child.

- Don't argue with your partner about the children in front of them. This will only increase their sense of guilt and blame about the break up.
- Communicate respect for one another when you are together and in discussion with the children
- Have faith in the other person's parenting abilities and distinguish between thoughts about the person as a partner and thoughts about them as a parent
- Find ways to share responsibility for everyday childrearing tasks, parenting, and movement between households.

"I find it helps to think and behave towards my ex in a more formal, business-like way."

(Moses, Liverpool)

The process can be helped if:

- parents can be realistic about how things will be and how long it will take to establish a new rhythm of life (Afifi and Hamrick, 2005);
- the complexities and challenges of co-parenting relationships are normalised;
- parents receive help in redefining the relationship from a romantic one to a co-parental one; and
- parents explore what shared parenting means.

Changing roles and responsibilities

New arrangements also mean accepting that parental relationships change. Non-resident parents must accept that their role has changed now that they no longer live with the child. Parents with care must accept some responsibility for actively facilitating contact arrangements, even if their own relationship with the former partner is fraught (Trinder et al., 2002). This was one mother's advice:

"... anything that helps them think about how the two adults are behaving is good. Even if the only contact they are having is the occasional phone call, or email, if they can make the contact better and reduce the level of conflict then this is better for the child."

(Katie, Bournemouth)

Managing feelings

Parents also need to find ways to contain the anger and hurt that they may be feeling if they are to establish a functional co-parenting relationship.

Parents who struggle to do so often remain caught up in issues related to the break down of the relationship, such as domestic violence (Wade and Smart, 2002) or conflict over contact and support arrangements (Adamsons and Pasley, 2005).

"Even though mum would always say something nasty about dad or whatever, she'd then say, 'but he's your dad, you know' and 'I'm sorry', and she would say to me, you know, 'you always...love your dad, I want you to love him' ...dad would always say, 'be good for your mum', even though they sort of hated each other they'd encourage us to be good and love the other one."

(Jack, Stoke-on-Trent)

If this is not possible parents might have to 'go their separate ways' for a while or find very structured and contained ways of communicating, for example, through email, voice mail or letters (Trinder et al., 2002). Once the heat of the anger has subsided then parents should be able to communicate more informally again.

New rules and rituals

When children move between households parents need to establish new rules and rituals for each home. Trying to agree the same rules for each household often leads to conflict. It is worth reminding parents that few rules need to be co-ordinated, as even young children can recognise that different homes have different rules. The most helpful 'shared' rules are bedtimes and allowances.

Section 4 outlines some of the additional pressures that couples forming stepfamilies face as they manage co-parenting at the same time as they establish new family relationships.

Key Messages

- As relationships break down they usually follow a predictable course from anger to apathy. In its final stages at least one or both partners will have disengaged from the relationship and moved on either physically or emotionally.

- A small proportion of children develop emotional, social and behavioural difficulties when parents' relationships are in trouble. In a minority of cases these difficulties are enduring. In most cases they are short lived.

- Parents and practitioners can minimise the impact of these stressful times on children by finding ways to manage conflict effectively; keeping children informed about what is happening; and by helping them to express their fears and feelings.

- Parents also benefit from help in re-establishing their relationship as parents rather than partners. Before they can do this, however, they are likely to need time to work out the ending of the relationship and tell their 'stories.

5. Understanding difference

- Between 1986 and 2005, the number of cohabiting couples doubled to 24 per cent of men and 25 per cent of women aged under 60.

- In 2005, 43 per cent of births in the UK were outside of marriage compared with eight per cent in 1971; of those births, 63 per cent were to cohabiting couples which means an increasing number of women are having children outside of a live-in relationship.

(National Statistics, 2006; 2008b)

The focus of this section is on family diversity. For the most part, it looks at the couple relationship in different family structures. It also touches on gay and lesbian relationships. Difference also includes the diversity of relationships across different cultures, races and ethnic groups. However, this publication does not address this broad issue for two reasons. First, much of the research has yet to be done that maps out the differences and similarities across the spectrum of race and ethnicity. Secondly, it is impossible to do justice to this diversity in the context of this publication. While many of the patterns and processes outlined so far will apply to couples from a range of cultures and races, some may not. This is particularly the case where the 'romantic' relationship is less important to the process of forming and maintaining relationships as, for example, in arranged marriages.

Changing families

The family setting into which children are being born has changed significantly over the last 30 years. Marriage has declined and cohabitation has become more common. Relationships have also become more fluid. A number of children will grow up with siblings born to different fathers. For practitioners working with a high proportion of lone parents, or parents in difficult or changing family circumstances, it might be tempting to think that the couple relationship is something of an irrelevance.

Changing family structures certainly mean that marriage is less common, and to some, less important. It also means that some family lives are more complex and involve relationships between current and previous partners, siblings and half-siblings, stepparents and step-grandparents. But where does this leave couples? Whatever the setting, the vast majority of parents will either be in a relationship, leaving one, or embarking on one. For example, just under half of the mothers in a national study who were not living with anyone at the time of the birth of their child were in a relationship. In a large-scale study of unmarried couples in the US, only 20 per cent of the unmarried mothers were single for the duration of the five year long study (Chase-Lansdale et al., 2004).

Being in a relationship, whatever its form, means that all those factors relevant to relationships remain important. If the relationship is going well each partner is likely to be deriving support from it. If it is going badly, partners are likely to be under stress. It is also true that different family structures will also bring different challenges. This is the focus of the next section. It provides an outline of some of the main challenges to the couple relationship that partners in different settings can encounter. The section does not cover parenting or wider issues relevant to changing families.

The section should be read in the context of the

patterns and processes that have been explored in the previous section. Some of the relationship patterns and processes relevant to couples under pressure are also likely to be pertinent to couples parenting in changing, and sometimes challenging, family structures. These include issues around coping, communication, conflict, and support.

It is difficult to avoid painting stereotypical pictures of different groups of people when bringing together research data. However, the information is meant to inform understanding rather than limit it. No doubt you will draw on your own experiences of working with families to provide a more rounded picture of the challenges some parents face, and the individual ways in which they approach them.

Young parents

- In 2005, 60 in every 1,000 15-19 year olds became pregnant in England and Wales.

- Approximately 7 in 1,000 13-15 years olds in Great Britain became pregnant.

(Brook, 2008)

The focus on young parents is often on the mother; on addressing the challenges of her circumstances and life-stage, and the risks to her and her baby's health. These challenges are often significant and can include, among others: poor education and employment opportunities, poverty, poor health, depression, and difficult housing circumstances (see, Swann et al., 2003). In the midst of these life strains and stresses young parents invariably have to navigate three major developmental phases – the challenges of adolescence, forming a partnership and the transition to parenthood (Gee and Rhodes, 1999).

The focus on the mother can mean that, sometimes, relatively little emphasis is placed on the relationship between the young parents. Many teenage fathers' accounts of their involvement with services show that they often feel 'dismissed' by the professionals caring for their partner (Quinton et al., 2002). But fathers have an important role to play. A teenage mother's involvement with a supportive partner is one of a number of factors associated with resilience in children born to teen parents (Werner and Smith, 1989; 1992; 2001). Fathers can be positive male role models for their children and an important source of support for the mother; support that has been linked to a mother's satisfaction with life (Unger and Wandersman, 1998), mental health, (Thompson and Peebles-Wilkins, 1992), self-esteem (Thompson and Peebles-Wilkins, 1992) and parenting (Crockenberg, 1987).

Involving the father is the first step in helping the young people to manage their relationship, either as partners or as co-parents. If the father is involved during the pregnancy he stands a better chance of remaining involved with his children if the relationship breaks down after the birth (McLanahan and Carlson, 2002).

Relationship challenges and processes
Fragility
Many young parents have high hopes for their relationships (One Plus One, 2006). In 2005, 74 per cent of babies born to teenage women outside marriage in England and Wales were jointly registered by both parents and 54 per cent of these parents were resident at the same address (Brook, 2008). Fathers are more likely to be committed to the relationship the older they are (Quinton et al., 2002).

But relationships between young parents are very vulnerable. Relationships appear to deteriorate rapidly over the first few years following the birth (e.g. Larson et al., 1996) and few mothers are involved with the father three years later (Gee and Rhodes, 2003). Only a third of children born to teenage mothers in the 1980s were with both natural parents by the time of the 1991 Census (Allen and Bourke Dowling, 1998). Where relationships are ongoing, they are often very 'on-off'.

The informality of these relationships can mean that when the relationship ends another one begins shortly after. If mothers have the support to think about the next relationship and what they are hoping for from it, they have a better chance of establishing a more lasting relationship next time around.

Although their relationships may be tenuous and short-lived, the loss of the relationship often has a detrimental impact on the mother's health and well-being (Gee and Rhodes, 1999; Berrington et al., 2007). Depression in young mothers can become enduring. Young fathers are also vulnerable to depression and anxiety early in the pregnancy, particularly in the second trimester (Spector, 2006). (See the earlier section on depression, page 58)

Box 2.8 Unmarried parents – 'Fragile families'?

The increase in the number of children born to unmarried parents has prompted researchers to ask whether these family structures are particularly fragile. A large, long-term study in the USA – the Fragile Families Study – has taken an in-depth look at unmarried parents. Their findings provide useful insight into the challenges these relationships can face. Although the research involved American parents, data comparing the ages and backgrounds of unmarried partners suggest that there are lessons to be learnt from the USA study (One Plus One, 2006).

Characteristics of unmarried parents in the USA Fragile Families Study

- Unmarried parents were younger than married parents, on average 23 years old, and many became parents in their teens with a previous partner.
- Both unmarried mothers and fathers were more poorly educated and had lower incomes than their married counterparts.
- In over half the partnerships one partner had a substance abuse problem, and in 10 per cent of relationships, both partners were dealing with addiction.
- A third of the unmarried fathers were incarcerated at the time of the birth.

Comparing married parents and unmarried parents the study found:

- relatively little difference in levels of conflict and in how supportive the relationship was;
- however, compared with 20 per cent of married couples who had broken up at five years, 42 per cent of cohabiting relationships and 74 per cent of non-residential relationships had dissolved; and
- 57 per cent of the non-cohabiting relationships had ended one year after the baby's birth.

Pressures on unmarried parents' relationships

Many of the relationships in the Fragile Families study broke down despite parents' high hopes that they would continue. Some of the factors associated with the breakdown of these relationships included:

- the mothers' distrust of men, especially men's unfaithfulness;

- depression of one or both partners;

- father's incarceration;

- material hardship that affected their ability to manage the daily necessities of life; and

- when the father had children from a previous relationship. Mothers in the study were unhappy that the father continued to see his previous partner because of ongoing involvement with his children. The mothers were distrustful of the relationship.

Other relationship problems common to young parents include high levels of conflict and domestic abuse, difficult break-ups, and disappointment over unmet expectations for financial support and help with caring for the children (Gee and Rhodes, 2003; Luster and Haddow, 2005). Some of these problems reflect the demanding circumstances in which many young parents live.

Financial support

The father's financial contribution is often a significant source of conflict and misunderstanding. Some mothers will see a father's lack of financial contribution as disinterest. And some fathers feel frustrated by their inability to contribute. As a result they withdraw from the mother and child, although the mother would welcome his involvement in different ways. For example, if the father took on some childcare responsibilities (see Herzog et al., 2007).

A father's financial capacity or earning potential is also a factor linked to young people's plans to marry. Some mothers are unwilling to marry unless they are sure that the father will be able to support the family (Edin et al., 2004).

Which relationships last?

A father is more likely to remain involved with the mother if he provided support during the perinatal period (Gee and Rhodes, 2003). Involvement with the mother predicts ongoing involvement with the child.

Another important factor is the relationship with the maternal grandmother. Many young mothers continue to live with their family. The grandmother often plays an important part in the day-to-day care of the infant, including providing regular childcare while the mother continues with her education or goes out to work. In many cases, the grandmother is the 'co-parent'. As such, fathers can find it difficult to establish their own parenting roles. And young mothers can struggle to continue the relationship with the father if her mother is opposed to it (Gee and Rhodes, 2003).

Family structures and relationship quality

Parenting alone

Of course, many young parents are lone parents, or lone parents for a part of their parenting careers. But lone parenthood is not always about age or finances. It might have followed widowhood, separation or divorce, or a short-term relationship. In some cases, supporting lone parents in their relationship might mean working with complicated relationship situations involving biological or step children from previous relationships (see Stepfamilies, page 89). Or, as above, working with fragile relationships that come under great pressure from the couple's difficult circumstances and the limited personal, social and economic resources at their disposal.

'Serial parenthood'

In the fragile families study, a third of children whose mothers were not in a cohabiting relationship at the time of the birth saw their mother go through three or more partnership transitions by the age of 3. Greater fluidity of relationships also means that increasing numbers of parents have children by two or more different partners (Carlson and Furstenberg, 2006). Children often struggle when the resident parent goes through a series of new and broken relationships. Each 'transition' - an ending or a new beginning – is associated with a modest increase in behavioural problems. But the effects accumulate with each change. Meaning that children who experience multiple transitions are at much greater risk of aggressive and anxious or depressed behaviour.

Complexity and stress

The stress on the mother and its impact on her mothering explain much of why children struggle with these ongoing changes (Osborne and McLanahan, 2007). The end of a relationship is stressful for those involved. More surprisingly, moving in with a new partner can also be stressful. Mothers ending a live-in relationship with a biological father or moving in with a new partner who is not the child's biological father often feel more stressed about their parenting than mothers living with a partner in a stable relationship (Cooper et al., 2007). Mothers who move out of one relationship and in with a new partner over a two-year period are generally exposed to twice as much stress in their parenting as those who experience just one relationship change in the year.

Diminished resources

Young, unmarried parents also generally have fewer emotional resources available to them. Fathers often become less involved when they have children with a new partner. For example, they may visit the non-resident children less frequently and provide little financial support (Manning and Smock, 1999).

The new relationship may also be less stable. For example, couples who have a child outside of marriage are less likely to cohabit or marry following the baby's birth if the father (but not the mother) already has children by a previous partner (Carlson et al., 2004).

Cohabitation versus marriage?

Cohabitation covers a range of relationships: a form of 'crash dating', a trial run, a prelude to marriage, or an alternative to it. Cohabitations are usually short lived and either dissolve or convert to marriage. Marriages preceded by cohabitation are more likely to break down. On the other hand, some cohabitations are 'marriage-like' and reflect similar levels of commitment and stability. What matters for the parents and the children, whatever the family form, is the quality of the relationships between family members. In general, there is little difference in the quality of relationships in long-term, committed relationships whether or not partners are married.

Research does suggest, however, that healthy family dynamics are more likely to occur in two-parent married families, as are positive child outcomes. This is partly because, on average, these families experience more stability, fewer stressors, and a greater level of long-term commitment on the part of the adults (Ambert, 2005). It will also reflect differences in attitudes, values, religious beliefs, and experiences of previous relationships. For example, individuals who have been married before are more likely to cohabit, and previous relationship breakdown is a risk factor for subsequent relationship breakdown.

Relationship breakdown is also more common because of the difficult circumstances and lack of resources available to a large proportion of, usually young, unmarried parents. These pressures make it difficult for them to maintain their relationships. (See Relationships Under Pressure, page 48).

Couple relationships in stepfamilies

- In 2001, 10 per cent of all families with dependent children in the UK were stepfamilies.

- 38 per cent of all cohabiting couple families with dependent children were stepfamilies, compared with eight per cent of married couple families.

- 80 per cent of stepfamilies comprised a natural mother and a stepfather.

(Census, 2001)

At its simplest, a stepfamily involves one of the adults being the parent of a child who is not related to the other adult. But this simple definition masks the complexity of stepfamilies. They can be made up of any number of children from either partners' previous relationship(s) as well as children born to the 'new' couple. Not surprisingly, one of the main challenges that stepfamily couples face is managing the complexity of their situations. For stepfamilies who sought therapy, one of the most

helpful aspects was learning about stepfamily functioning, including some of the myths surrounding life in a stepfamily (Pasley et al., 1996).

A note on language

The term 'remarriage' is used in this section to cover both married and non-married second partnerships where partners have formed a long-term, cohabiting relationship. It also reflects the fact that most of the research on stepfamilies has involved married couples as there is no formal way to identify cohabiting second or subsequent partnerships.

Managing chaos and complexity

Stepfamily members often fail to realise how complicated their family lives will be (Ganong et al., 2002). As well as developing and maintaining the relationship with a new partner, they may be maintaining ties with children from previous relationships; managing the relationship with a former partner; building relationships with stepchildren; and caring for a new baby. In fact, the early years of stepfamily life are noted for their chaotic quality.

"Our situation with 'my kids' and 'his kids' and 'our kids' is a case of learning as you go along. Just when it seems OK, something – or someone – upsets the balance. You have to live with it. I have rung a helpline for parents and talking it out with someone not involved helps me to cope."

(Anji, Oxford)

Failure to cope with the chaos and complexity can trigger a crisis (Pasley et al., 1996). Partners with good communication and conflict resolution skills are better placed to manage the challenges and chaos of the first few years of their stepfamily partnership.

The stages of establishing a stepfamily

Researchers have suggested that most stepfamilies need to navigate a series of stages in order to reach a level of stability and comfort in the new family. It begins, as do all new relationships with 'the fantasy':

"I had all sorts of romantic ideas about how it would be as their step-dad. But marriage didn't quite have the effect I was expecting. I wanted to adopt the kids but they didn't want to change their names. I was hurt but I understand better now."

(Keith, London)

Establishing the couple identity

The first stage for many stepfamily couples is living out the fantasy of a new relationship – the romance stage. But unlike many first-time couples, second partnerships do not have the luxury of a honeymoon phase that gives them time to establish their couple identity. They have to develop other relationships with stepchildren, former partners and other kin at the same time as they establish their own relationship. They also have to do that with an audience of children. In many cases, children may not want the relationship to succeed and may resent the changes it has brought, such as less time with their parent or less influence in the home.

Establishing the boundaries

There are also challenges involved in establishing and maintaining the boundaries of the relationship. When parents split up children often take on roles that the former partner held, such as confidante or carer of younger siblings. Establishing the new relationship will involve redefining these roles.

Getting on with former partners

There are also the challenges of establishing the couple relationship while renegotiating the role of

Figure 2.16: The Stages of Stepfamily life[7]

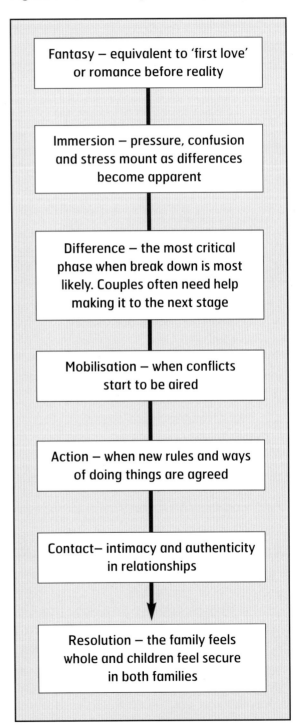

Fantasy – equivalent to 'first love' or romance before reality

Immersion – pressure, confusion and stress mount as differences become apparent

Difference – the most critical phase when break down is most likely. Couples often need help making it to the next stage

Mobilisation – when conflicts start to be aired

Action – when new rules and ways of doing things are agreed

Contact– intimacy and authenticity in relationships

Resolution – the family feels whole and children feel secure in both families

7. Adapted from 'Working with diversity' (Sure Start, 2002)

the former partner as a co-parent (Ganong and Coleman, 2004). How the parent and ex-partner get on can affect parents' well-being (Masheter, 1991), the quality of the new couple relationship (Buehler and Ryan, 1994), the child's relationship with both parents (Bowman and Ahrons, 1985), and children's adjustment (Amato and Keith, 1991). (See Section 'When things go wrong', page 74, for ideas on supporting parents).

The role of the couple relationship

Unlike in first partnerships, the couple relationship in stepfamilies has less influence on parent-child relationships. Stepchildren also have a comparatively strong influence on how parents get on, especially in the early years (Pryor, 2001). For example, a stepfather who is involved with a partner's children has a better chance of developing a more satisfying couple relationship (Adamsons, et al., 2007). It also means that couple issues are often inseparable from wider stepfamily issues, such as the parent-child relationship or the relationship with a former partner.

"I thought a lot about whether or not to remarry. In the end I felt Ken was mature enough to cope with my kids. He never tries to be their father but I know he finds it hard. Especially when they upset me, which all the kids do from time to time. On our own we talk about that and I tell him he's doing the right things."

(Wendy, Stockport)

Not trying to be like a first marriage

Some families experience problems because they are trying to base themselves on a first marriage model and hold misplaced expectations about family life. These include assumptions about:

- **stepchildren accepting stepparent's discipline without question** and before the emotional bond has been established;

- **how long it will take for the new family to establish itself** – Mills (1984) says you should tell families it will take as many years as the age of the child at remarriage – e.g. seven years if the child is seven. Although this may be an overestimate, it serves to temper expectations about becoming an instant family; and

- **how long it will take for stepparents and stepchildren to form a loving relationship** – unrealistic expectations can mean that stepparents do not employ the kind of effort and strategies that are needed to build relationships with stepchildren.

Baggage from the past

As Figure 2.2 on page 28 shows, everyone brings baggage from their past into a new relationship. Individuals embarking on a second or subsequent relationship may have extra baggage, however, from previous relationships.

Unresolved issues

Second or subsequent relationships are more likely to break down than first partnerships. One reason is that partners bring to the relationship the personal problems (e.g. substance abuse, depression) or personality characteristics (e.g. low frustration tolerance, impulsivity) that contributed to the failure of a previous relationship unless they have taken steps to resolve them. Similarly, partners may bring unresolved issues from a previous relationship that interferes with the new relationship, such as unresolved anger with an ex-partner or ongoing conflict (Ganong et al., 2002).

Unresolved fears

Fears about whether a new relationship will work can affect how partners communicate. For example, a partner may be so anxious to make things work that she is not able to be honest about her feelings, denies that problems exist and fails to resolve issues. This can leave one or both partners feeling alienated and powerless as the relationship suddenly deteriorates (Coleman and Ganong, 1985). This pattern may explain why some researchers have found very high levels of satisfaction in remarriage at the outset and much lower levels after six years (Coleman and Ganong, 2004).

It is also the case that remarried individuals appear to resort to divorce more quickly than those in first marriages when they are dissatisfied (Booth and Edwards, 1992). Providing timely support to second partnerships is an important element of avoiding a swift descent into relationship breakdown.

Finances

Many stepfamilies face financial hardship because of the multiple demands on a limited income. A major source of conflict is how those limited resources should be spent (Ganong et al., 2002). This is partly because the new couple's finances are tied up with those of former partners' contributions and spending decisions. Finances can become a place where conflicted loyalties between different family members are felt strongly. New partners can become frustrated by the lack of control they have over how money is spent (Ganong and Coleman, 2004).

Managing differences

Along with financial issues, other areas of conflict include:

- agreeing rules for children's behaviour and approaches to discipline;
- loyalty conflicts; and
- disputes with and about extended family members and former partners.

(Ganong et al., 2002)

Most disagreements reflect underlying tensions concerning negotiating boundaries around and within stepfamilies (Ganong et al., 2002).

The impact of a new baby

Relationships in stepfamilies can go through a whole new period of adjustment if a new baby arrives (Ferri and Smith, 1998). Although resident and non-resident children need time to adjust to the new baby, partners will also have their own particular issues to deal with. The following information has been adapted from the Sure Start Diversity Pack.

A new mother in an 'old family'

When the baby is a first for the mother but not the father, she will have to cope with the confusions of new parenthood as well as additional pressures. These may include:

- being haunted by the knowledge that her partner has been through this with another woman;
- struggling to feel in control of a process which her partner knows more about than she does; and
- resentment that her partner is spending time with his older children, especially if the mother thought that pregnancy might relax the ties to his first family.

An old dad in a new family

This may also be a difficult time for the prospective father as his own needs are squeezed out. For example:

- his partner may be anxious about the impending birth and expect one hundred per cent attention;
- his children may well have become angry or withdrawn;

- his ex may act out her feelings of betrayal and loss by stepping up demands around money or access arrangements; and

- he may be drawn to his 'new' family and withdraw from the old one just because it seems like the easier way out.

Or, in the experience of this mother, the father may become more withdrawn and attempt to compensate for the new baby by lavishing time or money on children from the previous relationship:

"I have been with Dave a long time, and it's probably a naïve view but I just thought that having Alex would change things. But if anything it has made it worse – now he has a child here it is almost like he feels he has to really overcompensate with the other kids. I am constantly doing everything really, and feel like I constantly have to fight Alex's corner too."

(Gita, Birmingham)

Relationships might also become more complicated with the ex-partner and grandparents as everyone adjusts to the new baby in the family.

Running on different cycles

The impact of a new baby on the stepfamily highlights the fact that family members often have competing needs as they move through different lifecycle stages (Pasley et al., 1996). For example, adolescent children may be seeking autonomy and independence while the adults are trying to build a tight family unit.

Gay and lesbian relationships

Fewer than 0.3 per cent of couples defined themselves as a same-sex couple in the 2001 Census (Duncan and Smith, 2004)

Similarities and differences

More similar than different

Reviews and one off studies have found that, in general, same-sex couple relationships are more similar to than different from heterosexual couple relationships (Patterson, 2000) Same-sex relationships are less stable than married relationships but rates of breakdown are similar to that of cohabiting heterosexual relationships.

Similarities

- studies have found no differences in levels of relationship satisfaction and the rate at which satisfaction changes (Kurdek, 1998);

- conflict resolution styles are similar across same-sex relationship and heterosexual relationships;

- same-sex and heterosexual couples appear to fight over the same things (Kurdek, 2004a); and

- the factors that affect same-sex partners' satisfaction in the relationship are similar to those linked to satisfaction in heterosexual relationships (Gottman et al., 2003).

Differences

- same-sex couples feel more autonomous and see fewer social or 'institutional' barriers to leaving the relationship (Kurdek, 1998);

- gay and lesbian couples are more optimistic and constructive during relationship conflict, such as suggesting possible solutions and compromises. They are also less likely to fall into the destructive 'demand-withdraw pattern' described earlier (Gottman et al., 2003; Kurdek, 2004b);

- they use more affection and humour when they bring up a disagreement and partners are more positive in how they receive it – tending to take it less personally; and

- they are also more likely to remain positive after a disagreement (Gottman et al., 2003).

Division of household labour

Although same-sex couples do tend to specialise in the household tasks they do, they are more likely than heterosexual couples to negotiate a balance between a fair distribution of household labour and each partners' interests, skills, and work schedules. This is even the case when couples have children living with them (Patterson, 2000).

Challenges

Social support

Same-sex couples are more likely to receive social support from friends than family members. The reverse is true of heterosexual couples (Kurdek, 2001). The lack of family support can be a significant source of stress in same-sex relationships and conflict around family of origin is common (Oswald and Clausell, 2005).

Hostility and stigma

Same-sex couples may be forming and managing their relationships in a wider context of opposition, homophobia, mis-understanding and fear than other couples. They may also be doing so at a cost to their family of origin relationships.

HIV and AIDS

The prevalence of HIV and AIDS in same-sex communities means that some partners will be dealing with the loss of a partner or friends. Others may be coping with a caregiving role and preparing for the possible death of a partner. Alongside this will be issues around the stigma attached to HIV and AIDS (Oswald and Clausell, 2005).

Intimate partner violence

Partner abuse in gay and lesbian relationships is even more hidden than in heterosexual relationships. Abused partners are fearful of disclosing it because of concerns about 'betraying' their community or reinforcing negative stereotypes about gay and lesbian relationships. Rates of partner abuse are higher in gay relationships and lower in lesbian relationships than in heterosexual ones (Ristock and Timbang, 2005).

Those who do report violence struggle to be believed or to be understood. The strongly gendered notions around heterosexual domestic violence mean that gay and lesbian partners can feel alienated by existing services. Gay and lesbian individuals who seek help may encounter homophobia or a lack of understanding of the different dynamics around the same-sex relationship. Indeed, some members of gay and lesbian communities cannot relate to the term domestic violence because of its association with male violence on women in heterosexual relationships (Ristock and Timbang, 2005).

Although many of the tactics used in abusive relationships are the same as those used in abusive heterosexual relationships, some behaviours are specific to the larger context of homophobia surrounding gay and lesbian relationships. These include: threats to reveal the sexual or gender identity of a partner to one's boss, landlord, or family member; threats to jeopardize custody of children because of a person's sexual or gender identity; and threats to reveal the HIV/AIDS status of a partner (Ristock and Timbang, 2005).

Children in same-sex families

Research has not found any important differences in the adjustment or development of children or adolescents who grow up in same-sex families. As in many other areas that investigate children's outcomes, the research indicates that the quality of family relationships is a more important factor in determining child outcomes than the parents' sexual orientation (Golombok and Tasker, 1996; Patterson, 2006). But, there are challenges to single sex parenting. Partners are functioning in a world that, in general, does not recognise or accept their family commitment (Laird, 2003). Most children in same-sex couples have just one legal parent. The second parent, usually the non-biological parent, can struggle to be treated as an equal parent. They usually lack any legal rights and responsibilities (Oswald and Clausell, 2005). The lack of legal recognition can also create problems if the couple separate.

A note on the research

Much of the research into same-sex couples has involved white, middle-class, well-educated gay and lesbian couples. The findings are therefore not necessarily representative of all same-sex couples, especially given how they, like all couples, vary greatly by class, gender, race, geography and other factors (Laird, 2003). Differences between same-sex and heterosexual couples may also be underrepresented because same-sex couple research has been dominated by the measures developed for and used with heterosexual couples (Oswald and Clausell, 2005).

Key Messages

- Changing family forms have created more complex and often more stressful situations in which to manage couple relationships.

- Couples in stepfamilies face a period of particular chaos and complexity as they establish their relationship. Pressure can increase if partners have a new baby. The birth invariably has an impact on the network of relationships in the close and extended family. Partners have to cope with the fallout of this pressure as well as come to terms with its impact on their individual roles and identities.

- Gay and lesbian partnerships are more similar to than different from heterosexual relationships, with small differences apparent in how partners may deal with conflict and the division of household tasks.

"I'm much more aware of what's going on now. Whereas before, you are aware of it, and you know you should address it but can't quite find the way in, now I feel actually able to raise the subject and know that I can deal with it positively."

(Community Involvement Worker)

Part 3: Tools for working with couple relationships

1. An introduction to working with relationships

Family practitioners, from social care, health, and other caring agencies, are often the first port of call for clients looking for help with relationship problems (Brannen and Collard, 1982; Ayles and Reynolds, 2001). As Figure 3.1 'Early Intervention' illustrates, when problems first arise, couples rarely talk about difficulties beyond their known circle of support. Few individuals seek help from professional agencies. For example, although 75 per cent of married adults with children in a BBC survey had experienced serious problems in their marriage, only eight per cent had sought help from a professional counsellor of any kind. In contrast, 53 per cent of parents in a recent survey felt that couples whose relationships come under pressure following the birth of a baby would benefit from more help from health visitors (YouGov, 2008).

However, family practitioners come under immense pressure as they deal with busy workloads, the complexities of different cultures and changing families, and difficult issues, such as domestic violence. Despite these pressures, given the right support, skills and framework, practitioners are well placed to provide this help (e.g. see Simons, 2003). And couples who receive help at these crucial times are more likely to weather the inevitable ups and downs of family life.

Figure 3.1: Early intervention

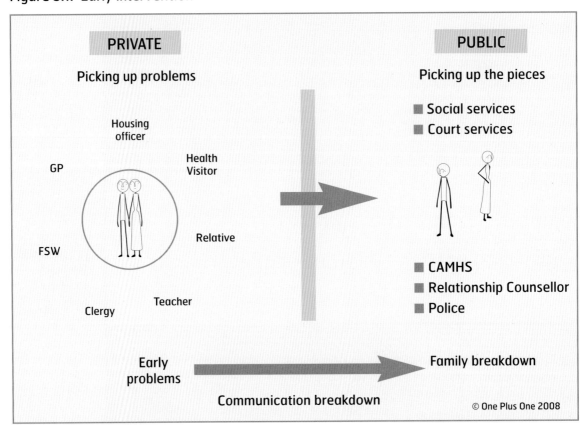

The Brief encounters® model

The Brief encounters® model is designed to enable you to respond to difficulties raised by clients within the course of your everyday work without getting overwhelmed by the demands this places on your time or personal resources. It provides you with professional guidelines that help you decide whether or not to help and, if you do help, how to support clients in finding their own solutions to the problems they face.

The following sections present the three stages of the helping model along with some essential skills and knowledge. This is not a guide to fixing relationship problems. Nor is it a guide to becoming a counsellor. It is about giving a client a 'window of opportunity' to voice their worries and feelings. And it is about feeling equipped to respond at these times.

"...there's no getting away from it, you're probably always going to be the first point of contact for most people who have a problem and it doesn't matter whether it's relationship or, you know, their hair is falling out, you've got to know really where you're going, what you're going to do with these people when they come and see you."

(Practice Nurse)

An overview of the Brief encounters® model

The Brief encounters® model is focused on the client's agenda and is designed to help you to listen to the client and manage the time you have to respond to him or her. Figure 3.2 provides an outline of the three stages of the BE model.

Figure 3.2: The Stages of a Brief encounter®

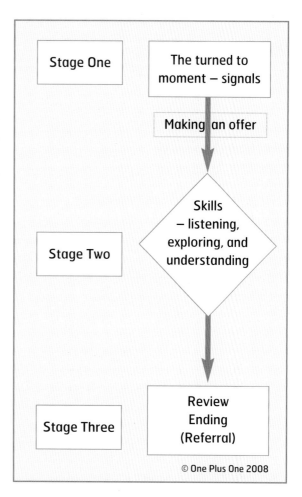

© One Plus One 2008

Box 3.1: Meeting the helper's needs through the BE model

To recognise and respond effectively to a client's needs for support you need:

- a framework for using listening skills within the context of your professional work;
- information about relationships, including the challenges they face and the way they change;
- to be able to decide whether you are able to deal with this problem or whether a client needs more specialist help; and
- ongoing support and supervision.

Stage 1 involves recognising and acknowledging a client's signal that she or he is seeking help and deciding how to respond, if at all, when your instinct tells you that a client needs to share something that is distressing them. Your decision to help will be influenced by a range of factors, including your personal experiences, the time available to you, and the setting of the encounter. Stage 2 is about helping the client to open up and share what is going on for them within the time that is available. As you draw things to an end you will enter Stage 3, which is an opportunity to review progress and think about 'what next'. The following sections explore each of these stages and the skills that underpin a successful brief encounter.

Web resources

You will find many of these skills demonstrated in a series of video clips available on One Plus One's website www.oneplusone.org.uk. You can also draw on resources that you can use with couples or that they can access themselves on One Plus One's site for couples www.thecoupleconnection.net. The site provides interactive information, resources and exercises for individuals and couples.

The case study

We are going to use a case study to illustrate the Brief encounters® framework in practice and help you explore some of the ways in which you might support parent and couple relationships. You will probably meet or have met and worked with couples in a similar situation to the couple in the case study so if it helps you to use a real life situation to understand the BE approach then please do.

Making the links – policy and research

At the end of each case study section there are references to the relevant policy and research, which have been documented in Parts 1 and 2 of this source book. These references will help you to understand the theory and evidence that is important in supporting couple relationships. It is recommended that you read the whole of Parts 1 and 2 as this will provide a sound evidence base to inform your practice.

Case Study

Family Background

Helen and Pete have been living together for two years. They met at school when they were 16 and moved in together when Helen became pregnant at 17. The pregnancy was unplanned.

Helen is white British. She had a difficult childhood as her mother was dependent on alcohol. Her father found it difficult to cope and left the family home when Helen was 3 years old and her younger sister was just a few months. Helen had little contact with her father after he left and learnt not to rely on others at a young age. Helen enjoys a closeness with Pete that she never had with her father. But she is also anxious that one day Pete might leave too. It makes her wary of getting too close or becoming too reliant on him.

Pete is Black British of Caribbean descent. He was raised by his mother, never knowing his biological father. His stepfather came to live with them six years ago when Pete was 13 years old. Pete has three stepsisters. He has a very strained relationship with his stepfather but is very close to his mother. Pete likes the way that Helen manages everything on her own, it reminds him of his mum. But he struggles with being a dad and he doesn't know how to get involved as Helen seems to have everything under control.

They have two daughters, Elsa aged 2 and Patsy aged 3 months. Pete works for a local removal company; it is heavy work involving long hours. Helen does some part-time work the Saturdays that Pete is around to look after the children. They live in a rented ground floor flat with a small garden. Like most young couples they are struggling with the challenge of life with two young children and making ends meet. They have some support from Pete's family who live 2 miles away, but Helen rarely sees her mother.

When their first child, Elsa, was born Helen suffered from postnatal depression and Connie (a family practitioner) supported them through that time. Since the birth of their second daughter Patsy, three months ago, Helen and Pete have been having difficulty with Elsa who is having temper tantrums.

Making the links:

Part 1 - The impact of the couple relationship (page 12)

Part 2 - What we bring to our relationships (page 30)
- Becoming parents (page 49)
- Depression and relationships (page 59)
- Young parents (page 85)
- Children and parental relationship problems (page 77)

1.1. Stage One – The 'turned to moment'

The 'turned to moment' – signals
Making an offer

a. Recognising the 'turned to moment'

The 'turned to moment' refers to those times when a client, often unexpectedly, looks to a practitioner for help or information about an aspect of family life that is worrying them. The approach might be tentative and designed to test out whether you are trustworthy and can 'really hear' him or her. It is often easier to raise worries in a light hearted way or under the guise of another issue, just as Helen did. In other situations a parent might make a throwaway comment: 'Oh, he always goes to the pub, when it's bedtime. So I put them to bed alone every night.' Or 'Do all families always argue about who is going to take the children to the park?' Many clients just respond to the question 'You look a bit down/tired – how are you?' by bursting into tears.

'Turned to moments' can come at inconvenient times, just as you are about to leave or during a busy clinic.

"With home visits, they always tell you while you are leaving. It's just when you're about to go through the door."

(Health Visitor)

Although you might be feeling under pressure, the chances are that if you do not respond to the help-seeking signal there and then you may not get another opportunity to deal with your client's concerns.

Stage 1a: The 'turned to moment'

Helen has come to her local clinic to see Connie and they have been talking about some of the ways in which Helen might handle Elsa's temper tantrums. Connie has also provided Helen with some information about the parenting classes available in her area.

As Helen is about to leave the clinic she tells Connie that, as a treat, the family are going to stay in a caravan at the seaside for the weekend. Connie wishes them a good time. Helen laughs and responds by saying "well that depends on the weather and if we can manage to get through the weekend without arguing." She went on to say that they can't seem to talk about anything without her exploding and Pete walking off.

Exercise
• How would you normally respond in this situation?

• Where do you think Helen and Pete might be on the 'Roller coaster of change'? (see Figure 2.9, page 48)

How might Helen be feeling?
Think about your own help-seeking patterns. What do you do when you are looking for support?

Making the links:
Part 1 - Couple relationships and parenting (page 16)

Part 2 - Difference and conflict (page 40)
- Relationship changes and challenges (page 36)
- 'The Roller coaster of change' (page 48)
- Supporting families when things go wrong (page 76)

b. Being aware of signals

It is important to be aware that your client will be presenting you with cues or signals that offer clues as to their state of mind. You will also have your own, internal signals. By being aware of signals, you are better able to recognise and respond to opportunities for support. Box 3.2 gives examples of signs you may pick up.

"Sometimes in an ante-natal clinic you notice a difference in them. They have been smoking heavily, look very peaked, haven't eaten or haven't done their hair or teeth. Then you start to pick up..."

(Midwife)

"They come in with odd physical symptoms sometimes. Or they come even with their children for little minor illnesses."

(GP)

Troubles at home can often be expressed through physical symptoms, depression or other 'somatic' expressions. Or children might become the focus. That might be either as scapegoats, so that they take the blame for broader family difficulties, or it might be that their own distress is apparent through emotional, physical or social difficulties.

The language that clients use will also give you a sense that things are not ok. They might say something like 'I've just had it up to here' or 'The kids are driving me mad at the moment.' But communication is more than just what people say. Their tone of voice, the feelings underlying what they say, or if they appear particularly sensitive or vulnerable, are all ways of communicating their distress.

Non-verbal communication is also important. It often provides a more accurate reflection about

---

Stage 1b: The signals

Connie recalls that when she last saw Helen in clinic she had also had her own 'internal signal' (intuition) that everything was not ok. Connie felt that there was something that Helen was just not saying, and overheard her saying to another mum that she was at the end of her tether and didn't know how much more she could take. She also noticed that Helen looked tired and anxious.

Exercise
• How would you respond to the signals Helen is giving out? If you decided to try and help, what would you say?
• What signals have you observed in families in distress? Think about each individual in the family, including the children, as well as how partners might be getting on with each other.

• What kind of words have clients used to indicate distress?
• What is going on inside you when you pick up signals that something is wrong?
• What signals do you give out?

Making the links:
Part 2 - Difference and conflict (page 40)

- Relationships under pressure (page 48)

- Becoming parents (page 49)

- When things go wrong (page 74)

how a client feels than the words that are being used. Some things to look out for include a client's facial expression, posture, hand movements, concentration levels, and eye contact. These cues are important signals to watch out for.

"So the tools and materials which showed us how to raise the issue, and how to become more aware of the issues really helped with my confidence. I'm much more aware of what's going on now."

(Health Visitor)

Although it is important to let a client know that you feel something is wrong and to give her an opportunity to open up, it is important not to push. Some people are happy to share thoughts and feelings whereas others find it difficult. If someone does not want to talk it is better to let it go but to show that the door is open ... 'If you need to talk just let me know.'

Box 3.2: Reading the signs

You may be presented with different indications that everything is not ok at home:

- A parent might seem withdrawn, distressed or agitated – signalling that they need to talk.
- They might display changed or problematic behaviour e.g. drinking a lot, verbal aggression, cancelled appointments, problems sleeping or a loss of appetite.
- Or they might make a series of appointments about apparently minor issues.

---

c. Setting the boundaries: choice points and making an offer

As we saw in the scenario 'the turned to moment' often happens when you are most under pressure, for example, when you thought you were coming to the end of an appointment. You can manage your own needs and pressures as well as those of the client by setting clear boundaries about what you can offer in a welcoming and positive way.

One of your first concerns will probably be whether you have the time to stop and listen.

"We've got too much to do and the thing is, you see, if you open something up, have you got the time to devote to it?"

(District Nurse)

However you become aware of a problem you will be faced with a choice to:

- acknowledge now and offer time now;
- acknowledge now and offer time later;
- acknowledge only, for example, with a touch on the arm or a word or look; or
- disregard the signal, for example, by mumbling something and changing the subject.

Making an offer

If you decide to acknowledge and respond to the signal, you will then need to frame an offer that sets out your working agreement. This is an offer of Time, Attention, and Respect. It usually includes:

- **an offer, such as an opportunity to talk (what)** – 'Would you like to talk?'; 'Can I help think things through?'

- an immediate response to the problem or offer of help at another time (when) – 'We could talk now?'; 'I have to make one visit but I could call back after that'; 'I could see you after school tomorrow.'

- a clear indication of how much time you can provide (how long) – 'I have 10 minutes now'; 'I have half an hour to spare at ...'

- finding a place that is ok for you both, even if that means standing in a quiet corner (where) – 'Let's just find a quiet corner here'; 'It's rather public here – let's go to my office'; 'Do you mind standing?'

The skills of listening and attending are important in making this offer. In this first stage of the model, you are beginning to use the listening skills of reflecting back. They help to set up your working agreement. (We cover more about listening skills in Stage 2.) It is also important to assess the limits of your competence and involvement at this stage. Clearly stating your intentions and checking that your client has ownership of the response, means that they can buy in to the working agreement.

If you do have just a few minutes to spare, it is possible to reframe time so that 2 minutes or 10 minutes seem like a gift rather than a snatched moment. Or you can explain that you do not have the time right now, but you would like to arrange a time to meet and talk. As you begin to set boundaries you will come to realise that explaining the limits on your time and resources will help to keep the discussion focused and productive, and limit your own anxieties about how you can move on once issues have been opened up.

Stage 1c: Setting the boundaries – choice points and making the offer

At this point Connie has a choice of how respond to Helen's turned to moment. Connie could choose to disregard the signal, perhaps deciding that she is too exhausted to offer Helen what she needs right now. Or instead, she can choose to acknowledge it and offer time later. Connie responded:

"It sounds like you and Pete are having a difficult time right now. Would it help if I popped in tomorrow and we could talk a bit more about what is going on for you? I have got half an hour tomorrow afternoon around 2 O'clock. How would that be?"

Helen agreed saying "Yes, it would be good to talk to someone about it. 2 O'clock is a good time because Elsa will be having her afternoon sleep."

This is the mini contract. It is an offer of time, attention and respect designed to help Helen find her own solutions. It is also designed to help manage a call for help within the context of your daily work.

Exercise
- How do you feel when someone turns to you for help?
- Write a list of the factors that might affect your decision to make an offer of help to Helen.
- Think about 'what to expect' if you did offer help. What might happen?

Making the links:
Part 1 - A changing workforce (page 21)
- The skills for working with families (page 22)

Box 3.3 summarises some points you might want to consider in framing your offer.

Box 3.3: Points to consider in framing an offer of help.

- How much time have you got?
- Can you create some privacy e.g. in a quiet corner or in an office?
- How are you feeling? Are you dealing with your own personal baggage, for example feeling tired, coping with your own distress or dealing with other unresolved issues?
- Would it be better to acknowledge the distress or signal and offer a time in the near future?
- How well do you know the client? What do you know about them already? What relationship do you have with them?
- What is your intuition telling you?

Reflective Activity

1. Think about a time when someone approached you in distress:

- Were you able to listen?
- What were you feeling? Were you feeling anxious about coping with the disclosure? Concerned about making things worse? Confident?
- Did you feel you had to come up with a solution?
- Were you able to set and stick to clear time boundaries?
- Were you able to go with the client's agenda?
- What can you learn from how you felt and how it went?

2. Look back at The roller coaster of change (Figure 2.9, page 48). Think about times of change that you have gone through:

- How did you feel?
- How did you get through it?
- What support did you receive?
- What support would you have liked to receive?

1.2. Stage Two – Listening, exploring, and understanding

Using skills - listening, exploring, and understanding

a. Listening

Listening is the basis of good communication and is important in offering support. Within the BE framework, it also means putting aside your own professional agenda in order to listen well. Usually, what a client needs most is someone who will really listen to them.

Really listening means fine-tuning your ear into what is being said. Concentrating absolutely to hear the content and feelings in the story you are hearing. It also means putting on hold for the moment all your own thoughts, anxieties and feelings – your role is to hear what you are being told, not to fix it or ask questions. You are tracking every word that is said and will have to stop the client from time to time to let them know what you have heard and what feelings are being expressed or hinted at. Don't ignore strong feelings or be afraid of them. They are the clue to the distress being experienced by the client. And remember, anger often masks great sadness, and conversely, sadness is often underlaid with anger.

Really listening to someone who is distressed or unsure about sharing is not easy unless you know 'how to listen'. Knowing how to listen includes possessing the skills, feeling confident in them, stepping out of 'fix it' mode and knowing how to manage boundaries, particularly the boundary of time.

A surprising number of clients seem able to get 'unstuck' and to help themselves after 'just listening' help. For example, according to parents, the most important feature of the support they received in a perinatal intervention run by midwives, was that the midwives were prepared to listen (Oakley et al., 1994). The support was linked to physiological and psychological health gains for the mother and the baby. Similarly a study of Health Visitors using active listening visits demonstrated how this helped women with postnatal depression (Cooper et al., 2003).

Box 3.4: How listening helps

Really being listened to can have a big impact:

- it gives us a chance to air feelings and to let off steam;
- allows us to express our needs and begin to talk about how some of these needs might be met;
- enhances our ability to face issues and feel strong enough to cope;
- supports us in being proactive and moving things forward;
- acknowledges how important the problem is; and
- helps us to find solutions.

Jenny, who valued the support she received from her community mother described it like this:

"She's a book with blank pages.... and I can see it, and I can fill in the blank page, yes, and I know that when she leaves here that book is closed and it is not opened again until she walks through that door."

(Jenny, York)

Guidelines for good listening

Try to concentrate on really hearing what someone is telling you. It is easy to be distracted by our own anxieties and the impulse to be reassuring.

Relax. Trying too hard can make us feel self-conscious and tense.

Repeat, or 'reflect back' what you have heard, to be sure you understood it. Let the client know that you are following her by repeating back, in your own words, what you think you have heard. Unlikely though it seems, it helps people to go on talking; it stops us interrupting before they have a chance to say what's really on their mind; and it helps the client to gain clarity and develop new insights.

Allow thoughtful silences. It is tempting to jump in during a silent moment. But pausing can give the client time to think, take stock, and process how they are feeling.

Pick up on and talk about the feelings that are being hinted at, especially strong feelings. Don't be afraid to voice feelings aloud and help to describe them. Clients need to hear what they have said. That means repeating back both the content and the feelings that are underlying the content. For example, a mother who says 'I can't stand it anymore' is sending a strong message that should

not be ignored. To acknowledge what you have heard you might reply 'You sound as though you're at the end of your tether.'

Cultivate a good attitude to listening. Whilst you engage in active listening, it is important that you are accepting, warm, genuine and non-judgemental in your approach, believing in the autonomy of the client. These attitudes help the client to clarify and amplify their own experience and its meaning. If you are too analytical about your client's situation, they may feel threatened.

Use self-disclosure cautiously. Talking about your own experiences can make the relationship more open and make you seem more approachable. But discretion is important. It is easy to fill the time with your experiences rather than those of the client. Moreover, sharing your own experiences before a client has had an opportunity to talk through theirs can be off-putting. A client needs to feel that she has your full attention and that you have not substituted her experiences with your own.

Avoid giving advice unless asked. People rarely take unasked for advice. Wait to be asked or make suggestions tentatively. 'Someone I know tried ... (or did) ... Do you think it might work for you?'

Keep focused on the point. You might be tempted to steer the conversation into more comfortable waters. Perhaps the subject is too close to your own feelings and makes you feel uneasy? If you decide that you are out of your depth it might be time to consider signposting the client to more specialist help (see Stage 3).

As you allow your client to tell their story by listening well and reflecting back content and feelings, you will be able to gain a better understanding of their situation.

b. What is really going on: the main message

Key skills

Skilled listening combined with empathic responses help to build rapport with the client. By using skills to build rapport, you will be able to acquire enough of the story from your client to establish what might really be going on. As well as reflecting back content and feelings, you might use other skills such as: affirming; normalising; acknowledging conflict; clarifying with the use of open questions; and offering prompts and probes. Some of these are explained in more detail below:

Integrating feeling and experience

As the guidelines on listening point out, an important part of listening is helping clients to identify and articulate their feelings and what has caused them. A simple way of helping clients to do this is to use the formula: 'You feel .... because ....'.

Clients might also need help in acknowledging their internal conflict – a mix of quite strong feelings. You might find it helpful to draw on the formula - 'You feel ...... but you also feel ......' – to help clients articulate this tension.

Asking questions

On the whole, asking questions means that you are directing the encounter according to your own agenda. If you really need to ask a question, for example because you did not understand what was said, make sure that they are open-ended questions. These kind of questions – which usually begin with a 'what', 'how', who' where', 'when' or 'why – are useful probes that invite a client to respond by elaborating on their feelings, experiences and behaviour. Closed questions, such as 'Are you sure you want to do that?' can be answered with a 'yes' or 'no' and do not always help people to talk. An open-ended question, 'What do you think will happen if you do that?' invites a fuller response.

Clarifying

Although all skills help a client to clarify their situations, you can use specific clarifying skills to help a client begin to think about her next steps. Clarifying also helps avoid the risk of misunderstanding or jumping to conclusions. You may do this by saying something like:

'Are you saying ....?'

'Do you mean ...?'

'I'm not sure I completely understood what you meant. Could you explain it again please?'"

The value of skills

These skills will help you to identify the 'main message'. Try and identify the main message by weighing up what you have heard and what you have observed. What is going on? What is really going on? You may have a real moment of insight and you will have to decide what is appropriate to share with the client. Your knowledge of relationships will also help you to decide what information and ideas it might be helpful to introduce in a sensitive way.

"For them, what they need is often very simple – it's just being listened to ... Listening skills are absolutely vital ... suddenly, almost, they will let themselves be a bit more open and relaxed and supported."

(Parenting Course Facilitator)

Resisting the temptation to 'fix it'

It can seem obvious to you as you work with a client what might help them to make progress in a situation. Many practitioners have been trained to fix things, but this can be a real obstacle to enabling a client to work out his or her own solutions. The temptation is to listen to just enough of what people say in order to understand the problem and then attempt to fix it for them.

Although you might be tempted to offer advice, the client will be clearer about how she might start to make changes and the outcomes are likely to be more positive if the client can be gently encouraged to seek her own solutions. This is the kind of collaborative and motivating support that parents say that they would like and which is most effective in helping them address change (Moran et al., 2004).

Stage 2a: What is really going on?

As promised, Connie visits the following day and gives Helen a chance to talk about what is really going on for her. Helen talks about how she has been feeling, she talks very rapidly for at least 5 minutes, about the state of the house and how she is feeling very tired and sleep deprived. Connie helps to draw out feelings by reflecting back, using phrases such as 'You sound really exhausted'. Helen hears the word 'exhausted' and confirms that is exactly how she is feeling.

Connie resists the temptation to jump in and offer practical solutions to 'fix it'. Instead she continues to reflect back and gently clarifies what she has heard, such as "So are you saying that how you feel now is different from how you felt after Patsy was born?" Helen went on to say that she felt certain she was not feeling as she had the last time when she had PND. Instead, she has been thinking about her parents a lot. She feels sad that her children might grow up not knowing their grandparents. She has thought about finding her Dad, but still feels angry with him for leaving her and her sister.

Helen feels that she can't talk to Pete about any

of this because she thinks that he doesn't really care and prefers to be out with his mates when he should be home with the family. She said she gets really angry with him and finds herself nagging and shouting at him all the time. Connie reflected this back by saying "You sound really overwhelmed by all that is going on right now". Helen nods and agrees that she feels she can't take any more. Feeling encouraged by being listened to, Helen continues to talk.

The main message

As Connie listens and continues to reflect back the story it becomes clear that Helen feels Pete is not as supportive as she thought he would be now that they have two children. She feels he does not understand how hard it is for her and he is spending more and more time at work. When he isn't at work he is out at the pub or at his mate's house, playing on the Playstation until all hours.

The helper's empathy

Connie's empathic response and use of listening skills by reflecting back the content of the story and the feelings Helen has expressed, helps

Stage 2a continued...

Helen to understand the situation and feel clearer about what is really going on. Connie is also able to draw on her understanding of how couple relationships work, together with gentle probes, to clarify the situation. The use of Stage 2 skills helps Helen to recognise that she and Pete have neglected their relationship, that they rarely spend time together and this is making her feel very anxious about whether or not the relationship will last. She has a deep fear that Pete will leave her and she will feel abandoned. Just as she did when her Dad left her as a child.

Exercise

- What feelings are likely to be around when there is conflict in a relationship?
- Look back to Part Two, Difference and Conflict (page 40), what are the common ways that people handle conflict?

- How would you encourage Helen to talk? What feelings are you likely to pick up on?
- Write a list of feeling words that might help you as you reflect back a client's feelings.
- What listening skills are you already using in your practice?

Making the links:

Part 2 - Virtuous and vicious cycles (page 45)
- Difference and conflict (page 40)
- What we bring to our relationships (page 30)
- Becoming parents (page 49)
- Economic pressures and work stress (page 63)

c. Moving the client on, staying within your boundaries

It can be daunting when you have given someone a space to open up to find a way to move on from the story to 'where next'... Some useful tips include:

- Summarise what has been said or help the client to summarise it. Starting to summarise usually begins the closure of this phase of exploring and understanding what is going on. It also increases understanding and encourages the client to begin to think about how she can help herself.

- Invite suggestions by asking 'How would you like things to be?' 'What would be happening if things were better?'

- Consider whether anything you have learnt about relationships, such as the stages through which they often move, might help the client to reframe their understanding.

- Invite clients to remember how they have resolved difficulties in the past. This is affirming and puts them back in touch with a more coping self.

- Recognise that some clients will feel unable to make changes but will feel relieved that they have been listened to and understood.

- Explain how much time you have left and how it might be helpful to review what you have covered and think about how the client might like things to change.

Taking sides

Although you might find yourself talking to both partners about a difficulty, you are most likely to find yourself listening to one partner's account. When you hear one account it is easy to start taking sides, even without being aware that you are doing so. You may have a natural connection with a female client or have been in a similar situation, in which case the client's story might stir up your own unresolved issues, often called 'personal baggage' (see Box 3.5). As Part 2 demonstrated, however, a relationship is a complex system and there is usually much more going on than is first apparent.

"I think then quite often you only get one side, you know, you get one side of the problem and so that can be difficult. Quite often I'm thinking, well, I wish I could see the other person."

(Community Mental Health Practitioner)

In many cases partners become stuck in their positions and find it hard to take on board what the other person is saying. If you are able to listen without taking sides, you can help clients to air their grievances and see how they might put things right. When people feel understood they can then begin to reconnect with the person who has upset them.

Summarising

Summarising is an important tool. It helps you to:

- pull together what you have heard;
- demonstrate to the client that you have been listening to what has been said;
- help the client to organise their thinking and you to organise yours; and
- clear up any misunderstandings or inaccuracies about what has been said.

It also helps you move the encounter on and start the process of thinking about how things might change – Stage 3.

Box 3.5: 'Personal baggage'

Everyone has had personal experiences, the stuff of their own history. It can help us to empathise, or it can make us want to avoid certain subjects. If you find this happening, it might help to think about whether:

- You are having difficulty managing your own feelings. Where might you get support?
- You are afraid you won't be able to cope with the client's feelings, or of being swamped by their demands. What do you need to do to feel enabled?
- You aren't confident about your own skills. Where might you get further training or support?

Stage 2b: Summarising and moving into Stage 3

There are about 10 minutes left until the end of the visit. As Helen has told her story and things have become clearer, Connie begins to summarize what she has heard, saying:

"You've shared a lot today let's gather this up. Where have we got to? It seems like you are feeling weighed down looking after the children. You and Pete have been spending very little time together. You are worried that you are drifting apart and your main worry is that Pete might leave you. Have I got that right?"

Connie would like to move Helen towards thinking about how things could change and what she could do to bring about those changes. Connie mentions that they have five more minutes and brings things together: "It really sounds as if you'd like things to be different."

Exercise
- What have Helen and Pete brought to the relationship that might be making it difficult to adjust to this new stage of life now?
- Look back at the 'Changes and stages of relationships' (Figure 2.6, page 38), what stage could Helen and Pete be at?
- Now that the underlying issues have been uncovered how would you help Helen and Pete to move on in this situation?

Making the links:
Part 2 - Adult relationships and attachment (page 32)

- Changes and stages of relationships (page 38)

- The roller coaster of change (page 48)

Figure 3.3: The circle of thoughts, feelings and behaviours

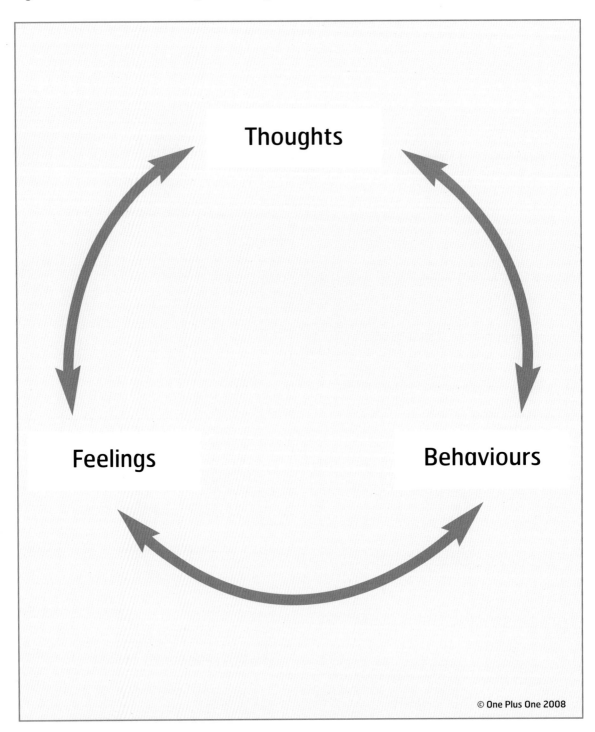

© One Plus One 2008

A helpful resource: The circle of thoughts, feelings and behaviours

Although not a core part of the Brief encounters® framework, 'the 'circle of thoughts, feelings and behaviours' is a useful tool to use with clients in helping them to explore what is happening.

Our thoughts feelings and behaviours are interacting with each other all the time and each has an impact on the others. We are normally very aware of our feelings (whether we are angry, upset, worried or happy) and the majority of our behaviours – what we do – but we are not always aware of how our thoughts are affecting how we feel and what we do. Beck (1967) believed that the way people think influences the way they feel and the way they behave. Therefore, a depressed person might have negative or depressive thoughts ('I'm useless', 'Nobody cares about me'), which, in turn, have a negative impact on their feelings and behaviour. Encouraging a client to explore the way that thoughts, feelings and behaviours are linked can help her to consider how she thinks about her partner and increase her understanding of what may be happening in the relationship.

"I remember one mum said 'So then, in that case, when my husband comes home from work and he is slamming the door and he is snappy and what have you, then in that case, that's him feeling angry then, isn't it? He must be having angry thoughts!' It was a big light bulb moment for her – you could almost see the penny dropping. 'So I wonder why he is feeling so angry?' she said. She had never really thought about it before. As soon as we drew the picture which showed how thoughts, feelings and behaviour interlink, and said that people's behaviour will tell you something about how they are thinking, she realised something about what was going on that she hadn't realised before."

(Parenting Course Facilitator)

Box 3.6: Using the circle of thoughts, feelings and behaviour

At the end of a long day, during which Elsa has really played up, Helen has cooked dinner but there is no sign of Pete. Pete has still not arrived home – he is two hours late. He is consoling a workmate who has just been made redundant but Helen doesn't know this.

They are both very tired and things have been a bit difficult in their relationship. Helen immediately thinks 'he's so selfish, he doesn't care about us, he's down the pub again' (thoughts). She feels angry and resentful (feelings) and when Pete does come home, she shouts at him and storms off to bed (behaviour). He responds by getting angry as well (feelings) and by saying it is no wonder he's late if all she does is nag him (thoughts and behaviour). They don't make up and barely speak the next morning.

Connie meets Helen the next day at clinic. Helen blurts out what has happened and how upset she is feeling. Connie stays with how Helen is feeling, empathises and lets Helen know she has understood how she feels. As she talks with Helen, Connie draws on Beck's circle of thoughts, behaviour and feelings. She chose to 'enter' Beck's circle by focusing her attention on feelings. As Helen got her feelings 'off her chest' she was able to think about the evening more calmly. Connie was then able to move to talking about Helen's thoughts. As they talked Helen could begin to see (thoughts) that if she had not assumed that Pete was late for selfish reasons she would not have got so angry about everything. (Helen and Connie both accepted that it is easy to think the worst when you are already feeling let down by your partner.)

The next day Pete was late again. Things went differently:

Thoughts: Helen decided not to assume the worst and waited to see why Pete was late …

Feelings: Although she felt hurt Helen did not feel as angry as she had done the day before.

Behaviours: When Pete got home Helen greeted him. She managed to stop her hurt feelings overwhelming her enough to ask about his day. He explained that everyone had been asked to stay late to talk about the job cuts at work and he hadn't had a chance to ring. He also explained what had happened the previous evening. Helen was able to share how upset she felt when he was late because she found the days with the children so difficult sometimes and it seemed like he didn't really care. Pete apologised and said he would not go out with his mates tomorrow night but would try and get back from work in time to help with putting the children to bed.

A different scenario…

If Helen's distress was caused mainly by Elsa's behaviour, Connie might have decided to focus on behaviour rather than feelings. By suggesting a small behavioural change for Helen, such as introducing a reward chart, the children's behaviour might improve – creating hope (thoughts) and leading to more positive feelings about her self as a mother and her children and increasing confidence in helping to change behaviours for both herself and her children.

Making the links:

Part 2 – Difference and conflict (page 40)

– Same but different (page 44)

Reflective Activity – Good Listening Skills

1. Think back to a time when you felt you used good listening skills:

- What made it a good experience?
- What factors have you identified that are important in good listening?
- Now compare them with the listening skills outlined in this section.

2. Think about a time when you have revealed how you are feeling to someone else:

- What did they do?
- How did it make you feel?
- What, if anything, could they have done differently?

1.3. Stage Three – Review and ending

Review, Ending, (Referral)

Taking the next steps

As you reach the end of the time you have available to be with a client you will need to draw the conversation to a close. Reviewing where you have got to sets the stage for thinking about 'where next?'

a. Making changes

Some clients may want help to make changes in their lives or relationships but it is very normal to feel ambivalent about the need to change. Every existing and new situation has costs and benefits attached to it. Skilled listening can help an individual find the motivation for change and begin to see how things could be different. Motivation is key. Focusing on what is motivating a client rather than why they do not want to change can help a

Box 3.7: Principles of Motivational Interviewing

- Resist the righting reflex
- Understand the persons' motivations
- Listen with empathy
- Empower the person

client to move forward. For example, you might want to consider drawing on motivational interviewing techniques (Rollnick, Miller and Butler, 2008).

This non-confrontational technique is useful for those who are undecided about changing or cannot see a way forward (Morrison and Bennett, 2006). Motivational interviewing "allows the person to explore and discover the advantages and disadvantages of their behaviours for themselves" (Rusch and Corrigan, 2002 page 28) and tip the balance in favour of change.

Box 3.8: Helping change happen

If a client seems to be 'stuck' and reluctant to change you may find some of these simple motivational techniques helpful.

Ask the Miracle Question

Suppose you woke up tomorrow morning and a miracle had occurred while you were asleep and the problem had disappeared: How would you know a solution had arrived? How would it be different? How would you feel? What would you notice first? How would other people know? or, If you could wave a magic wand what would you wish for?

Importance and Confidence

Scales are used that explore importance and confidence:

- On a scale of 1 to 10 how important is it to...?
- On a scale of 1 to 10 how confident are you that you could...?

The points chosen on the scale give an indication of the person's readiness to change. This is a starting point to explore, and tip the balance in favour of, making the change by asking questions directed towards increasing motivation and confidence.

- You gave yourself a score of 'importance' of 5, why not 1?
- What would need to happen to move you from a 5 to a 7 or 9 say?
- What do you think would help your confidence score to move up from 3 to 6?

Constructing Possibilities

- What are the possibilities as to what you might do next?
- What else...?
- What other things...?
- What do you think you could do to make it better?
- What were you both doing when it was going well?

b. Setting goals

Once the client has clearly identified and 'owned' the problem she may need help in setting goals to work towards. Goals are clear statements of what a person wants to do or achieve and they form part of the client's action plan. They spell out how to handle some or all of a difficult situation. They need to be – specific, measurable, achievable, realistic and timely: SMART. Your affirmation will be important in helping a client to feel positive about achieving the goals that you agree together. Although they are something that is more often associated with counselling, even in a brief encounter this information can help a client to move on.

Stage 3a: Developing an action plan

Connie summarised the main message and Helen indicated that she really wanted things to change. In reviewing progress Connie used the following questions as a framework:

Helen
- where is she now?
- where does she want to go from here?
- what resources are available to her?

Helen recognises that there are a lot of things going on in her life and understands why she is feeling overwhelmed. She realises that her harsh criticism of Pete is what usually starts the arguments and that Pete is probably also feeling fed up and upset. The more criticised and upset he feels the more time he spends away from Helen and the children. Helen decides that she wants some support and would like to spend more time with Pete.

Helen mentions that her neighbour has offered to babysit many times but she has never taken her up on it. Helen admits that all her life she has had to rely on herself. She finds it hard to ask for help and usually refuses help when it is offered as she doesn't want to be seen as a teenage mum who can't cope. Connie normalises the need for help after having a baby and encourages Helen to think about what the benefits of accepting help might be. Helen begins to think that this would give her and Pete some time alone and also give her some time to herself. Helen comes to the decision that it is worth giving it a try and decides to ask her neighbour if she could babysit next week, after they get back from their weekend away. She thinks she might offer to pay the neighbour or get her a small gift, so that she doesn't feel as though she is taking advantage of the situation. Helen also resolves to talk to Pete about how she is feeling about their relationship.

Connie asks whether there is anything else that might help things to change. She remembers that Pete's mother has offered to come once a month and take the children to the park to give her a bit of time to catch up at home. She did this after Elsa was born. She has not taken her up on the offer because she has been too preoccupied. Connie wonders if Helen feels that this support could be helpful and explores this with her.

Affirmation
Affirmation will also be important. Connie might want to remind Helen of the things she has achieved in the past, such as "I seem to remember you made time for yourself when you were coping with postnatal depression. Pete was really helpful then when you talked things over with him."

Connie
As Connie reviews progress with Helen she will also review her own responses and feelings:
- where am I now?
- where do I want to go from here?
- what resources are available to me?

continued...

Exercise

- Connie and Helen have come a long way in this half hour. How do you think this conversation could be brought to an end?
- What would make it a good ending?

Making the links:

Part 2 - What we bring to our relationships (page 30)

- Difference and conflict (page 40)
- Young parents (page 85)

Issues to consider in a review

In your review you might want to consider the following issues:

- How serious and pressing is the situation?
- Do you feel able to cope with the client's difficulties by listening and perhaps offering information and tentative suggestions?
- What other sources of help are available e.g. self-help groups, family or friends?
- Would the couple benefit from more specialised help?
- Are you familiar with the services available in your area?
- Do you feel confident in helping the client or do you lack knowledge, confidence or support?
- Are you aware of factors that might prevent the client from seeking specialist help?
- Have you 'left the door open' for her to come back to you?

Stage 3b: Ending

As the brief encounter draws to an end Helen says she feels better now that she has been able to share her worries and understand what is happening. Helen has an action plan to help her work on her relationship with Pete.

Connie reminds Helen that she can get in touch at any time if she feels the need to. She also leaves Helen and Pete the details of the couple connection website. Here they can have a chance to check out some of the challenges couples face when they become parents and complete some of the exercises that are designed to help them work things out together.

Exercise

- How might Connie be feeling after her time with Helen?
- What might have come up for Connie?
- Go to **www.thecoupleconnection.net** and familiarise yourself with the information, activities and guidance that has been provided for couples.

Making the links:

Part 1 - Couple relationships and parenting (page 16)

Part 2 - The roller coaster of change (page 48)

c. Signposting and referral

Sometimes you might feel that it is right to refer a client on to more specialist help. That decision will be affected by your personal experiences, current situation and the demands upon you, as well as the client's story. Although your instinct might tell you to refer on very early in the encounter, it helps to allow enough time to let the story unfold before making a hasty decision.

One reason to refer a client on to specialist help is when their difficulties have come to a head or a 'crunch'. When couples hit a crunch it usually means that ongoing problems have not been dealt with and the relationship has run into serious trouble. (Part 2 describes some of the patterns of communication that you might observe in clients who are struggling with more enduring relationship difficulties.) As you support more clients in their relationships you will become more able to differentiate between those who have hit a 'pinch' – a tricky patch – and those in a 'crunch'. Working with the latter will feel more challenging and you will probably feel out of your depth. Understanding these differences can help you to be more confident about the limits of your role and protect you from becoming overwhelmed by more complex relationship problems.

When to refer?

As well as working out what stage a couple might be at, Figure 3.1 'Early intervention' on page 98, gives you some insight into the point at which clients may be willing to take up support from formal or public agencies. Are problems still private or have they moved beyond that stage?

If you do decide to refer the client elsewhere, how you do so is crucial. It takes courage for a client to share her feelings and concerns. Being given information about other agencies or being referred on can feel like a rejection, that in some way the referrer wants to get rid of you.

"There are cases where you say 'I can't cope with this, I'm going to have to refer you on'. And they almost seem to withdraw, back off, as if to say 'I don't want to see anybody else, I want to speak to you'. That is very difficult because you don't want to walk out and leave them there in limbo."

(Health Visitor)

Skills for referral

Moving someone on to another person or service requires great sensitivity. When someone is referred sensitively they know that they have been listened to and understood. They are also reassured that the referrer has thought about what is likely to be most helpful, is informed about what the agency can offer, and supportive of the referral. All this means that the client is more likely to take up a referral.

The skills used to refer clients on or signpost them to other services include all the listening skills used in inviting disclosure and exploring the client's initial difficulties. If you use these skills you are more likely to disengage effectively and to help the client engage with new sources of support.

Referring on – knowing the client

Clients need information about what to expect from the organisation or individual that they are referred to, including practical information about costs. What will be offered? What are the working methods? What are the expected boundaries and benefits? Your decision to refer will also be influenced by what you know about his or her circumstances. Other issues are listed in Box 3.9.

Referring on – knowing your options and being connected

You have a better chance of encouraging a client to take up a referral or follow up a recommendation if you have a working relationship with the helping agency, understand what is on offer, and can explain it to the client. Your feelings about the effectiveness of relationship counselling or other referral options will also affect how successful you are in encouraging a client to take up services. You might want to think about inviting a counsellor or representative from the organisation to come and talk to your service to find out more about what they have to offer and how they operate.

"And I would think really there's no substitute for actual sort of face to face interaction with somebody to say, 'Y'know this is what we offer, this is what we're able to do. If you want to refer a client to us this is what will happen'. That kind of background."

(Relate Counsellor)

Your network of colleagues may be able to offer you support, advice and information about local services and helping options. Creating and maintaining relationships with colleagues and networking with other disciplines will protect you against professional isolation and give you a range of options to explore for clients. This will also help you to keep up to date with what services are available. There is nothing more dispiriting for a client than approaching a service only to find that the service has moved, closed down, or changed its remit.

> ## Box 3.10: What types of services are available?
>
> Appendix 4 lists a number of national helping organisations. Useful services include:
>
> - Relationship support services, such as Relate or Marriage Care;
> - A counsellor in a local health centre or independent counsellors;
> - The Couple Connection website **www.thecoupleconnection.net**;
> - Helplines;
> - National or local befriending and support groups, such as Gingerbread, Home-Start or Cruse;
> - The General Practitioner or the Community Psychiatric Nurse; and
> - Less obvious options, such as employment assistance programmes or assertiveness training groups.
>
> You might want to draw up a list of local or national agencies in these different categories with telephone numbers, websites, waiting lists, costs etc. Try to make sure it is accurate and up to date.

The Couple Connection website offers interactive information, resources and exercises that users can work through alone or with a partner. It also provides an opportunity to talk about relationships with other users. It is evidence based, drawing on One Plus One's 30 years of experience in investigating what makes relationships work – or fall apart – and using those findings to support and strengthen couple and family relationships.

Supporting the referral or signposting

You may also want to consider how best you can support a client through a referral or in contacting another agency:

- As a practitioner, are you going to keep the 'door open' even after referral?
- Have you got another role with that family?
- Will you need to offer support whilst the referral is being taken up?
- What is the likely impact of this referral for the client?

What if the client does not go?

However skilful the referral process, clients still default. It is helpful to accept this and understand something of their experience. It may be, that despite all the right support, the timing was wrong for the client. She might not have been ready or able to deal with the challenge that disclosure and possible change creates. Or it may be, more simply, that practical reasons took over, such as problems with cost, transport or childcare.

And finally ...

Working with clients from different cultures

No doubt you have already built up an understanding of issues relevant to supporting clients from different cultures or groups in your daily work. You may come across situations and issues where you would ordinarily provide the listening support of a brief encounter. However, counselling, from which the Brief encounters® approach has evolved, is a very western approach to dealing with personal problems that has grown out of acceptance of the growth of individualism. Not all cultures see talking over difficulties as an acceptable or useful way of addressing personal problems. Some clients will expect advice, education, or information, but not a time of listening! d'Ardenne and Morrod (2003) identify some other potential stumbling blocks, including:

- a Western focus on the significance of past events versus a non-Western focus on the present;

- the changing state of the family in the West versus the importance of traditional family values in some other cultures; and

- a Western focus on the individual versus the role and obligations of the individual to the community in other cultures.

You may want to think about how your attitudes or experiences influence work with clients from different cultures.

- Can you accept, acknowledge and understand the client's culture?

- Are your expectations or assumptions about the client's culture likely to affect the support you provide or the outcome of the support?

Looking after you

Peer support and supervision are vital elements of the support you provide to others. Support helps you to keep in touch with yourself. Being aware of your feelings provides valuable clues about the client, your relationship with them, your own barriers to referral and your personal competency. Support (see Proctor and Inskipp, 1993) can provide you with the opportunity to:

- share your work in confidence;

- get feedback and guidance;

- develop your professional skills, ideas, and information;

- let off steam if you are angry, fed up or discouraged;

- acknowledge the feelings that a client can stir up in you and how your own 'baggage' may be affecting your response; and

- receive support in coping with those feelings and in observing patterns of behaviour – both your own and those of clients.

Many of you will already have access to supervision that enables you to take better care of yourself and, as a result, better care of clients and their partners. If you do not have adequate arrangements in your area, think about using the Brief encounters® skills – listening, attending, and empathising – to set up peer supervision. You might also want to seek out training to increase your skills and confidence.

Reflective Activity: A Brief encounters® recap

Telling the story – what is going on?

Understanding – what is really going on?

Desired outcome – how would it look if it was better?

Action plan – how can we make it better?

Think about a time when a client raised a pressing emotional or relationship worry.

- What signals did you pick up about the client's need to talk?
- How well did you help them to tell 'their story'?
- Did you find out 'what was really going on'? If so, how did you do that? If not, what could you have done differently?
- Did you manage to move on from the story and start thinking about how things could change? How did you do that?
- How were things left?
- What worked well? What would you do differently next time?

Key Messages: A checklist

- Address relationship problems routinely. You have lots to offer including: time, attention and respect; a real ability and wish to listen; the knowledge and skills to normalise problems where appropriate; and support that promotes self-help.

- Respond to signals of distress. Listening skills give you a breathing space and the opportunity to really hear what is going on for the client. Put your own views and anxieties on hold and remind yourself you do not have to 'solve' this problem.

- Don't pursue the issue if clients are unwilling to share their problems with you or if you are dealing with too much personal baggage.

- Keep in touch with yourself. Being aware of your feelings provides valuable clues about the client, your relationship with them, your own barriers to referral and your personal competency. It also helps to remember that practitioners also give signals about how busy or open they are, how much they care or if they are judging what they hear.

- Check out information on local service providers, including how they operate, what they provide and their referral criteria. You are unlikely to follow up signals if you expect to get out of your depth and have no idea where to send your client for help.

- Remember the value of mutual support between other colleagues and disciplines.

- Consider how to respond positively to clients who do not take up a referral. 'Going for special help' is never easy, can create a sense of stigma, and requires a great deal of trust.

Appendices

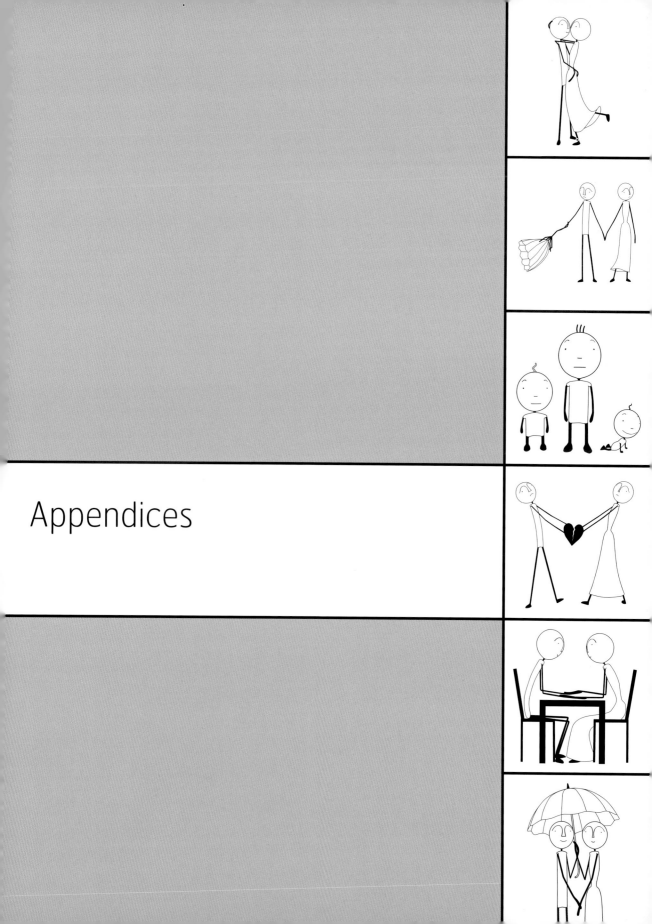

Appendices
Appendix 1: Policy Timeline

Date	Publication or initiative	Details
1998	**Supporting Families** (Home Office)	Labour Government's first consultation paper setting out its vision for family support.
2003	**Every Child Matters** Green Paper	The Green Paper forms the foundation of Government policy towards children and parents after the Victoria Climbie report. Proposals include Children's Trusts, improved information sharing, Common Assessment Framework, Sure Start Children's Centres, Extended Schools, Young People's Fund and Children's Commissioner. And sees the introduction of five clear outcomes to which services will work – 1. Be Healthy, 2. Stay Safe, 3. Enjoy and Achieve, 4. Make a Positive Contribution, 5. Achieve Economic Well Being.
2004	**Chief Nursing Officer's Review of the Nursing, Midwifery and Health Visiting Contribution to Vulnerable Children and Young People**	The review assesses the role of midwives, nurses and health visitors in delivering the ECM agenda and identifies 13 areas for change, including promoting integrated working, and enhancing workforce skills and capacity.
2004	**National Service Framework for Children, Young People and Maternity Services**	Guidance published by the DoH setting out a child-centred approach to health with a particular emphasis on supporting parents (Standard 2). It outlines a ten-year programme for sustained improvement in children's health and well-being through setting standards for the care of children, young people and maternity services. It is designed to form an integral part of the Every Child Matters: Change for Children programme.
2004	**The Children's Act**	The legal underpinning for Every Child Matters with youth justice, education, health and social services placed under a duty to co-operate together and share information about children under their care.
2004	**Choosing Health** White Paper	Reiterates the importance of parents in improving children's health.

Date	Publication or initiative	Details
2005	**Children's Workforce Strategy: Building a Worldclass Workforce for Children, Young People and Families. Consultation document**	A consultation document setting out the Government's vision for creating a workforce that is able to produce the outcomes proposed in ECM. To do so, it acknowledges the challenges it is currently facing re recruitment, integrated working, skills, and leadership and outlines how it proposes to tackle them. The vision highlights a flexible workforce with fluid boundaries and responsibility for children's well-being extending across a range of professionals e.g. criminal justice, teaching, early years, social work. As such, it recognises the crossover between its aims and the NSF.
2005	**Common Core of Skills and Knowledge for the Children's Workforce Prospectus**	Sets out basic skills and knowledge expected of the workforce in six areas of expertise: • effective communication and engagement; • child and young person development; • safeguarding and promoting the welfare of the child; • supporting transitions; • multi-agency working; • sharing information.
2005	**Support for Parents: The Best Start for Children** (Treasury)	Treasury report reaffirms the Government's commitment to giving children the best start in life through: helping parents to meet their responsibilities; an emphasis on progressive universalism; prevention and early intervention strategies. Policies arising out of these principles include: actions to promote family's economic stability; support for parenting and support aimed to help parents manage the work-life balance; reforming public services to deliver services relevant to families' needs.

Date	Publication or initiative	Details
2006	**Respect Action Plan**	The Action Plan announced a range of measures to tackle social exclusion and anti-social behaviour. These include: the setting up of a National Academy of Parenting Practitioners (Autumn 2007), appointing parenting experts in 77 areas; establishing Family Intervention Projects in 50 areas; and Health-led parenting support pilots in 10 areas (November 2006).
2006	**Early Intervention Parenting Pathfinder Projects**	Testing 'evidence-based' parenting courses in 18 Local Authorities amongst families of 8-13 year olds.
2006	**Reaching Out: An Action Plan on Social Exclusion**	Cabinet Office publication – highlighting the importance of parenting as a factor in improving the outcomes of children.
2006	**Parent Support Advisers** introduced in 20 Local Authorities and 600 schools	PSAs originally formed part of a pilot to support children and families where there are early signs that help could be beneficial. The Children's Plan (2007) promises to expand the service.
2006	**Parenting Support Guidance** for Local Authorities published	Asking LAs to develop parenting support services through a parenting support strategy that informs the Children and Young People plans and takes account of parents' views with the aim that LAs have a Parenting Commissioner and strategy in place for March 2007.
2006	**Pilots of Health-led parenting project** announced by DoH and DCSF	Pilots carried out in 10 Local Authorities drawing on David Olds' Nurse Family Partnership Programme delivering intensive support to vulnerable new parents, largely teen parents, for two years during pregnancy and following the birth.
2006	**Parenting experts appointed in 77 areas; Family Intervention Projects** established in 50 areas to work with most hard-to-reach	Initiatives announced in RESPECT Action plan to improve support for the most disadvantaged and hard-to-reach families.

Date	Publication or initiative	Details
2007	**Policy Review of Children and Young People: A Discussion Paper**	Discussion paper published by the Treasury ahead of the 2007 Comprehensive Spending Review bringing together the evidence for the review.
2007	**Making it Better for Mother and Baby** (DoH)	The DoH report by Sheila Shribman sets out a new vision for maternity services and emphasises joined up services delivered within the community and addressing the broad range of parents' needs, particularly the most disadvantaged.
2007	**Every Parent Matters** (DCSF)	The first document setting out current and future policies relating specifically to parents and parenting. The focus is on supporting parents in promoting their children's learning and development across the years. As well as initiatives to improve access to childcare/ information about childcare, it outlines current and future measures to support parents such as Sure Start, SS Plus advisers for teenage parents, extended schools, TIS, PSA, and FIPs.
2007	**Maternity Matters: Choice, Access and Continuity of Care in a Safe Service**	Setting out the Government's vision for maternity services – their role in delivering Every Child Matters and the NSF standards. Emphasis on parental choice and improving outcomes among disadvantaged and marginalised women e.g. BME, teenage pregnancies.
2007	**Building on Families: Progress** (Prime Minister's Strategy Unit)	This policy review document highlights 3 areas for action/ policy: supporting families by providing through targeted help and information as well enabling parents to meet their responsibilities; supporting a healthy work-life balance; supporting the most hard to reach by tackling the causes and consequences of social exclusion.

Date	Publication or initiative	Details
2007	**Aiming High: Supporting Families** (Treasury)	Treasury review of services for children and young people, including disabled children and their families. The review identifies 4 key areas for action including: building children's resilience through investment in services e.g. Children's Centres; providing more personalised services that reflect the needs/views of users; reaching the hard-to-reach; tackling cycles of low achievement. It also reiterates the Government's commitment to supporting stable parental relationships in order to maximise beneficial outcomes for children as well as supporting children in cases where parents separate.
2007	**Facing the Future: A Review of the Role of Health Visitors**	Sets out the findings of a review, chaired by Rosalynde Lowe, of the role of health visitors. It places an emphasis on progressive universalism and child health teams comprising a range of staff, including nursery nurses, and headed up by experienced health visitors who would focus on work with families requiring more specialised or intensive support.
2007	**National Academy for Parenting Practitioners launched**	Announced as part of the RESPECT agenda the NAPP is aimed at improving the skills of those involved in working with parents and encouraging the delivery of parenting programmes with a strong evidence base for their effectiveness.

Date	Publication or initiative	Details
2007	**The Children's Plan: Building Brighter Futures** (DCSF)	Setting out the Government's vision for children over the next 10 years based on the Department's strategic priorities with a range of targets to be achieved by 2020. Measures include an increase in the numbers of Parent Support Advisers in Schools and the appointment of 2 parenting support experts in each Local Authority. The plan is grounded in Children and Young People Today, which brings together the evidence for the development of the plan.
2008	**Think Family: Improving the Life Chances of Families at Risk** (Cabinet Office)	Sets out the Government's vision for a whole family approach to support that sees adult and children services working together around the needs of the whole family.
2008	**Child Health Promotion Programme** (updated) (DoH and DCSF)	An updated version published of the early intervention and prevention public health programme that is integral to universal services for children and families.

Appendix 2: Information on training for work with couples

One Plus One provides an essential accredited foundation programme Brief encounters®. This is a three day skills based training programme that builds on much of the material presented in this source book. OPO also offer an innovative interactive training resource – My Mum and Dad argue a lot – to help practitioners work with parents dealing with conflict. A cartoon based Picture Kit is available that can be used by practitioners as a starting point for discussions with parents about many of the common issues that cause problems in couple relationships.

Workshops are provided by our highly skilled trainers and details can be found at www.oneplusone.org.uk/training

Marriage Care offer an initial training course each year designed for students with little or no previous knowledge of counselling in couple relationships. It leads to a Diploma in Relationship Counselling jointly awarded by Marriage care and York St John University. They also offer fast track for those trained and practising as a counsellor who wish to add couple counselling to their portfolio.

www.marriage care.org.uk

Tavistock Centre for Couple Relationships (TCCR) provide a broad range of courses for those wanting to increase their understanding of relationships. They range from short courses about specific topics such as working with parent relationships, to qualificatory programmes in Psychodynamic Couple counselling at Introductory, Masters and Doctorate level.

www.tccr.org.uk/training

Relate also have a range of courses at local centres across the UK. The Working with Couples: An Introduction to Theory and Practice is a three month course for practitioners wishing to work as Relate couple counsellors and who have previous experience and qualifications in the field of counselling.

www.relate.org.uk

Appendix 3: Statistics on family life

Marriage
- The average age of first marriage is 32 for men and 30 for women (National Statistics, 2008a)
- The majority (70 per cent) of divorces are to couples where it is the first marriage for both (National Statistics, 2008a)
- 68 per cent of divorces are granted to women, the most common reasons are behaviour, adultery, or separation for at least two years (National Statistics, 2008a)

Children
- 53 per cent of divorces involve children. In 2005, 136,000 children under 16 experienced their parents' divorce (National Statistics, 2008a)
- In 2006, 44 per cent of live births were registered outside marriage (National Statistics, 2007a)

Lone Parents
- 23 per cent of dependent children live in a lone parent household (National Statistics, 2008b)
- 92 per cent of lone parents are women, eight per cent are men (National Statistics, 2008b)

Stepfamilies
- 10 per cent of families are stepfamilies (National Statistics, 2007b)
- When forming stepfamilies most children will stay with their biological mother and her new partner. In 2006, 84 per cent of children living in stepfamilies were living with their biological mother (National Statistics, 2008b)

Cohabitation
- 22 per cent of the population is currently in a cohabiting relationship (Barlow, 2008)
- 36% of the population has been in a cohabiting relationship at some point (Barlow, 2008)
- 56 per cent of cohabiting couple relationships end in marriage (Barlow, 2008)
- 20 per cent of all live births in 2006 were jointly registered to couples outside of marriage living at the same address (National Statistics, 2007a)

Ethnicity
- Cohabitation is most common in White British, Mixed Race and Black Caribbean families (National Statistics, 2006b)
- Married couples families are highest in Indian, Bangadeshi, Chinese, Pakistani and Other Asian groups (National Statistics, 2006b)

Appendix 4: A guide to further resources and helping organisations

Adoption

Adoption UK
http://www.adoption.org.uk

Supporting adoive families before, during and after adoption.

British Association for Adoption and Fostering
http://www.baaf.org.uk

UK charity working for children separated from their birth families.

Post Adoption Centre
http://www.postadoptioncentre.org.uk

Advice, counselling and support to anyone affected by dealing with the challenges and opportunities of adoption.

Child abuse and neglect

International Society for the Prevention of
Child Abuse and Neglect
http://www.ispcan.org

Supporting individuals and organisations to protect children from child abuse and neglect.

NSPCC
http://www.nspcc.org.uk

Working to end cruelty to children.

WAVE Trust
http://www.wavetrust.org

Uses business strategy principles to reduce violence and child abuse around the world.

Children and Young People

4Children
http://www.4children.org.uk

4Children aims to ensure that all children and young people (0-19) get the support they need in their local community.

Children in Scotland
http://www.childreninscotland.org.uk

The national agency for voluntary, statutory and professional organisations and individuals working with children and their families in Scotland.

National Council of Voluntary Child Care Organisations
http://www.ncvcco.org

Ensuring the wellbeing of children by promoting the voluntary sector's contribution to the provision of services.

The National Children's Home
http://www.actionforchildren.org.uk

Children's charity providing services in the UK since 1869. Originally National Children's Home.

Young Voice
http://www.young-voice.org

Promoting the rights of young people under The UN Convention on the Rights.

Children with disabilities

NHS Direct
http://www.nhsdirect.nhs.uk

Provides 24-hour health care - delivering telephone and e-health information services day and night direct to the public. They can also be called on 0845 4647.

Direct Gov
http://www.direct.gov.uk

The Direct Gov health and wellbeing pages provide information on health and well-being, health services, illness and conditions, carer advice and on mental health.

Contact a Family
http://www.cafamily.org.uk

Contact a Family is the UK's nationwide charity providing information and advice to parents of disabled children.

Mencap
http://www.mencap.org.uk

Mencap supports people with learning disabilities, their families and carers.

Great Ormond Street Hospital and the UCL Institute of Child Health
http://www.gosh.nhs.uk

Great Ormond Street Hospital and the UCL Institute of Child Health provide guidance on helping children cope when a brother or sister is in hospital.

Action for Sick Children
http://www.actionforsickchildren.org

National registered charity, founded over forty years ago at a time when parents were actively discouraged from staying with their child in hospital and visiting hours were very restricted. The site offers helpful advice and information. Today the charity focuses on national issues together with its network of branches, who also work locally to improve health services for children and young people.

Counselling and support

British Association for Sexual & Relationship Therapy
http://www.basrt.org.uk

Provides information about psychosexual counsellors throughout UK. They can also be contacted on 020 8543 2707.

Thecoupleconnection.net
http://www.thecoupleconnection.net

Thecoupleconnection.net provides online support for parents through information, social networking and private personal and couple spaces where couples can work on their relationship together.

Supportline
http://www.supportline.org.uk

Provides emotional support and details of counsellors, support groups, and agencies throughout the UK. They can also be contacted on 020 8554 9004.

2 As 1
http://www.2as1.net

Provides relationship support to couples and individuals. Service is aimed at Britain's Black community, although welcomes all people regardless of race, gender, religion, disability or sexual orientation. 2 As 1 can also be contacted on 0700 2222 700.

Institute of Family Therapy
http://www.instituteoffamilytherapy.org.uk

(London based) Provides couple and family therapy service for those who are finding relationships problematic. They have a sliding scale of fees. They can also be contacted on 020 7391 9150.

Marriage Care
http://www.marriagecare.org.uk

Provides listening and information service for people facing difficulty in their marriages, families or close personal relationships. Also offers face to face relationship counselling throughout England and Wales and referrals to other services as appropriate. You can telephone them on 0845 660 6000.

Relateline
http://www.relate.org.uk

Relateline is a helpline service for individuals and couples with relationship difficulties. It offers counselling and support service, information and referrals to the other 94 Relate centres throughout the UK and to other services as appropriate. Call Relateline on 0845 130 40 10.

Dealing with affairs and jealousy

50Connect website
http://www.50connect.co.uk

Website targeted at the Over 50's, providing information and advice on how to survive an affair.

Armchair Advice site
http://www.armchairadvice.co.uk/relationships

Offers articles about why people are unfaithful, separation and divorce, and how to get over an affair.

Domestic violence

Women's Aid
http://www.womensaid.org.uk

Women's Aid is the national charity working to end domestic violence against women and children.

Family Organisations

Care for the Family
http://www.careforthefamily.org.uk

Strengthening marriages and supporting families.

Family and Parenting Institute
http://www.familyandparenting.org

Information and support for parents.

Family Links
http://www.familylinks.org.uk

Promotes emotional literacy, nurturing and relationship skills in families, schools and communities.

National Council on Family Relations
http://www.ncfr.org

An educational forum for family researchers, educators and practitioners to share in the development and dissemination of knowledge about families and family relations.

National Family Learning Network
http://www.campaignforlearning.org.uk

Provides information and support to family learning practitioners.

General health

Association for Post - Natal Illness
http://apni.org

Provides a telephone helpline and information leaflets for sufferers and health care professionals as well as a network of volunteers, who have themselves experienced post-natal illness.

Disability, Pregnancy and Parenthood International
http://www.dppi.org.uk

Disability, Pregnancy and Parenthood International (DPPI) is a small UK charity controlled by disabled parents promoting better awareness and support for disabled people during and after pregnancy, and as parents.

Disabled Parents Network
http://www.disabledparentsnetwork.org.uk

Disabled Parents Network is a national organisation of and for disabled people who are parents or who hope to become parents.

Down's Syndrome Association
http://www.downs-syndrome.org.uk/

Help for people with Down's Syndrome, and information, reassurance and support for the families of new babies with Down's Syndrome.

FPI - Family Planning Association
http://www.fpa.org.uk

Sexual Health charity working to improve the sexual health of all people throughout the UK.

Mental Health Foundation
http://www.mentalhealth.org.uk

Aims to help people survive, recover from and prevent mental health problems.

MIND
http://www.mind.org.uk

Mental health charity working to create a better life for everyone with experience of mental health distress.

National Deaf Children's Society
http://www.ndcs.org

Provides support, information and advice for deaf children and their families.

Postpartum Support International
http://postpartum.net

Helping families overcome postpartum depression.

The Centre for Child Mental Health
http://www.childmentalhealthcentre.org

For anyone interested in the emotional wellbeing of children and young people.

Young Minds
http://www.youngminds.org.uk

A nationl charity committed to improving the mental health of all children and young people under the age of 25.

General Support

Citizens Advice Bureau
http://www.citizensadvice.org.uk

Helping people solve their legal, money and other problems with free, independent and confidential advice.

Samaritans
http://www.samaritans.org

Confidential, non-judgemental support 24 hours a day.

Grandparents

Grand Parents Association
http://www.grandparents-association.org.uk

Support and advice for grandparents.

Grandparents Plus
http://www.grandparentsplus.org.uk

Provides information and news and aims to raise the profile of grandparents providing care.

Legal advice

AdviceNow
http://www.advicenow.org.uk

Advice on the law and your rights.

Children and Family Court Advisory Support Service (CAFCASS)
http://www.cafcass.gov.uk

Looks after the interests of children involved in family law proceedings.

Community Legal Advice
http://www.communitylegaladvice.org.uk

Provides free legal information, leaflets and fact sheets for local legal aid advisers and a legal aid calculator.

National Family Mediation
http://www.nfm.u-net.com

Offering mediation to couples, married or unmarried, who are in the process of separation or divorce.

Resolution
http://www.resolution.org.uk

An organisation of 5,000 lawyers and family justice professionals committed to the constructive resolution of family disputes.

The Children's Legal Centre
http://www.childrenslegalcentre.com

An independent national charity concerned with law and policy affecting children and young people, providing legal advice, information and representation.

Networks

Mumsnet
http://www.mumsnet.com

Online meeting point for parents.

Netmums
http://www.netmums.com

Netmums provides local and national information for mums (and dads), including childcare vacancies, play places and reviews of maternity units.

Parentschat
http://www.parentschat.co.uk

Parents Chat is a meeting place for UK mums (and dads) to join together and share their experiences with other parents.

One parent families

One Parent Families | Gingerbread
http://www.oneparentfamilies.org.uk

Supports lone parents.

Single Parent Action Network
http://www.singleparents.org.uk/

An organisation of single parents working to improve the lives of one parent families.

The Centre for Separated Families
http://www.separatedfamilies.org.uk/

Offering support, training, advice and information to everyone affected by family separation.

One Space
http://www.onespace.org.uk

Provides information and advice for single parents.

Parenting

Dads Space
http://www.dads-space.com

Provides information and advice for dads.

Parentline Plus
http://www.parentlineplus.org.uk

A national charity working for and with parents. Parentline Plus works to offer help and support through a range of free, flexible, responsive services. They can also be telephoned on 0808 800 222.

Gotateenager
http://www.gotateenager.org.uk

A website providing support and social networking for parents of teenagers.

Dad Talk
http://www.dadtalk.co.uk

Supports fathers through social networking and information provision.

Meet a Mum Association
http://www.mama.co.uk

MAMA provides support for mums feeling isolated or depressed after the birth of a child.

Relate for Parents
http://www.relateforparents.org.uk

Provides SMS and online support for parents.

For Parents By Parents
http://www.forparentsbyparents.com

Information and support provided for parents by parents.

Home-Start
http://www.home-start.org.uk

Provides support to any family who needs it, as long as they have at least one child under 5.

Parents As First Teachers
http://www.parentsasfirstteachers.org.uk

Trains professionals to work with parents and children aged 0-5, providing information, support and encouragement.

Parents Centre
http://www.parentscentre.gov.uk

Information and support for parents on how to help with a child's learning, including advice on choosing a school and finding childcare.

Pink Parents
http://www.pinkparents.org.uk

Pink Parents is a national support project for lesbian, gay and bisexual families, offering a range of support services and social activities.

PIPPIN
http://www.pippin.org.uk

PIPPIN provides programmes and classes which support men and women through the emotional process of becoming a parent.

Positive Parenting and Children
http://www.ppclondon.org.uk

Working with families affected by HIV/Aids.

Raising Kids
http://www.raisingkids.co.uk

Raising Kids offers practical parenting advice and information on child nutrition, child development, parenting skills and education.

Transition to parenthood

BBC's Parenting pages
http://www.bbc.co.uk

The BBC's Parenting pages have information and advice on getting pregnant and having a baby – it includes support for parents.

Direct Gov
http://www.direct.gov.uk

The Direct Gov website has pages that include information on having a baby, including healthy eating and registering the birth of your child.

The Baby Centre
http://www.babycentre.co.uk

The Baby Centre can help plan a pregnancy, birth and track the development of your child. It includes hints, tips and tools on various aspects of pregnancy and parenting.

Baby World
http://www.babyworld.co.uk

Baby World has information and advice on trying for a baby, pregnancy and becoming parents.

Bounty
http://www.bounty.com

Bounty is an online resource centre for pregnancy and birth including information on pregnancy, birth and childhood.

Association of Breastfeeding Mothers
http://www.abm.me.uk

Offers breast feeding counselling and support.

Breastfeeding Network
http://www.breastfeedingnetwork.org.uk

Breast feeding support and information.

Cry - sis
http://www.cry-sis.org.uk/

Support for families with excessively crying, sleepless and demanding babies.

La Leche League
http://www.llli.org.uk

Breast feeding support, encouragement, information and education.

Midwives Online
http://www.midwivesonline.com

Provides evidence-based information to advise, support and enhance the experience of expectant parents and their families.

National Childbirth Trust
http://www.nct.org.uk

Pregnancy, birth and parenting charity providing telephone helplines, local support, courses for parents and general information.

OXPIP
http://www.oxpip.org

Supporting parents and infant relationships.

Tamba
http://www.tamba.org.uk

Information and mutual support networks for families of twins, triplets and more.

Tommy's
http://www.tommys.org

Aimed at parents-to-be, those thinking about trying for a baby and parents who have experienced problems in pregnancy.

Work and childcare

Daycare Trust
http://www.daycaretrust.org.uk

Working to promote high quality, affordable childcare.

National Childminding Association
http://www.ncma.org.uk

Promoting home-based childcare for the benefit of children, families and communities.

National Day Nursery Association
http://www.ndna.org.uk

Aims to enhance the development and education of children in their early years.

Sure Start
http://www.surestart.gov.uk

National and local childcare information.

Working Families
http://www.workingfamilies.org.uk

Organisation offering help and information on how to balance family life and employment.

Appendix 5: Relationship resources for working with individuals or couples

1. The circle of thoughts, feelings and behaviours

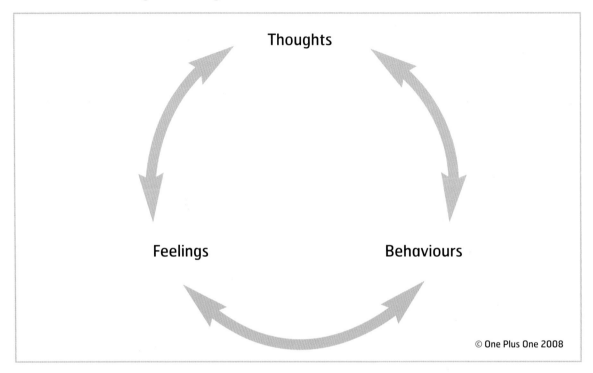

© One Plus One 2008

Using the circle of thoughts, feelings and behaviours

- 'The tendency to assume the worst'. When things are not going well, partners often assume the worst about the other's behaviour. You can use the circle to help clients explore this pattern and what is underlying it. For example, a partner may have had an affair at some point in the relationship and the client thinks that when he is late home he has been with someone else. Or the client may have had a previous relationship that ended badly and is tempted to interpret her current partner's behaviour in the context of what she experienced in her previous relationship.

- 'Getting stuck in negative cycles'. Couples can also get trapped in negative cycles of thinking and relating. The circle might give them some insight into more positive cycles. You could explore these negative cycles using the vicious and virtuous parenthood cycles in Part two.

- 'Re-framing'. People with 'negative' frames tend to see the world as hostile and see the worst in other people. This outlook, often apparent in depressed or aggressive people, can end up de-motivating a partner and further eroding a client's self-esteem and wellbeing. The circle is helpful in supporting a client to reframe a world view – her sense of herself and her partner.

2. Basic communication skills for couples

You might also find it helpful to keep in mind some basic tips on how couples can help themselves.

- Keep lines of communication open wherever possible.
- Make time to really listen to each other – to try and get into the 'other person's shoes'.
- Choose a good time to talk. Avoid raising a problem just as your partner has walked through the door or when one of you is in the middle of something.
- Try and raise an issue gently rather than going in on the attack.
- Remember both partner's views and feelings are equally important.
- Think back to how you used to sort things out before the pressures and tiredness of looking after a baby or taking care of a family.
- Don't give up – things can change and what seems difficult this week could be different next week.
- Just because you are arguing now it doesn't mean you will always argue.
- Equally, it is impossible for two people to agree all the time and it is natural to have differences, especially when it comes to being a parent.
- Try different approaches.
- If you can't get out easily, talk to a friend or relative on the phone or send an e-mail – someone who won't take sides – a midwife, a health visitor or other practitioners who work with families can also be a good person to talk to.

3. Discussion topics for working with new parents

Helping parents to identify and address the issues that put pressure on the relationship helps to prevent partners blaming the relationship itself. The following list outlines some of the topics that practitioners have found it helpful to explore with new parents.

What we bring to our relationships
- Family-of-origin experiences, such as conflict between parents and family breakdown;
- The individual characteristics of each partner e.g. temperament, expectations, gender ideology, personal identity. Discussing these issues helps parents to address how their characters are affecting their parenting and their relationship.

Managing the relationship
- Being prepared for an increase in conflict i.e. conflict management style, intimacy, emotional regulation as well as skills for conflict;
- Helping couples see the positives in one another and in their relationships;
- Helping couples find time together.

Roles and expectations
- Current and postnatal expectations around household work, childcare, parenting style, paid work, and involvement of friends and family;
- Partners' readiness to take on a parenting role.

Pressures and support
- The other pressures that couples are dealing with, such as health problems, financial pressures, lack of local support, postnatal depression;
- The type of support available from the extended family.

Understanding the changes
- Exploring loss and change, particularly antenatally e.g. fear about loss of intimacy, sexual attractiveness, energy, earnings, and interest in each other. Parents will benefit from being helped to generate ideas about how they will reclaim some of these perceived losses as time goes on;
- Normalising what partners are experiencing, including the emotional disturbances and changes in the relationship.

Appendix 6: How can we help clients with sex-related issues?

- Listening with an open mind. It helps to remember 'Don't assume anything!' and just to remind you again of the need to be sensitive. You may be working with someone who has been sexually abused, and you can seem like an abuser if you are not sensitive. The art is to find a balance and be able to encourage them to talk about sex.
- Raised awareness. Be aware of the link between sex and relationships and listen to what's going on in the relationship
- Listening for underlying feelings. Remember the link between feelings and behaviour. When things aren't going well you will often pick up feelings of resentment, anger, guilt or anxiety. Unjustified guilt or anxiety can be carried over from childhood or adolescent experiences and block sexual functioning.
- Understanding. Try to understand 'what is going on?', and 'what's really going on?'
- Normalise. You may be able to help the client see the situation in context and 'normalise' their experiences.
- Giving permission and reassurance that it is ok to talk about sex, to enjoy/not enjoy sex. Possibly to try out what may have seemed to them unacceptable behaviour.
- Help communication. By helping them to talk and being comfortable, maybe providing some words or language to use, you may encourage the client to talk with their partner. Communication can lead to greater assertiveness as well as improved sex.
- Inform. You can undo some of the myths and impossible expectations people have and also give some information about gender issues.
- Useful suggestions. You could help couples to think about privacy (bedroom door-locks), or trying out different positions. Maybe to think more about foreplay for men as well as women. For some couples a timetable or contract can create some space if a partner is very demanding.
- Referral. Don't try to go it alone. You are not expected to be a sex expert. Have you got ideas about where you might refer a client with sex or relationship difficulties that you know?

Appendix 7: Good practice guidance on domestic abuse

Good practice guidance suggests that any response to a disclosure of domestic violence should ensure that:

- you create an environment in which a client feels comfortable talking about abuse. This includes offering privacy and reassuring her of confidentiality, while explaining the limits of your confidentiality when it comes to child protection issues;
- the client is left feeling believed and empowered; that the abuse has been condemned and that she has not been judged or blamed;
- the client is given enough time to reach her own conclusions – giving time is one of the most supportive things a practitioner can do;
- you find out more information gently, using open-ended and non-threatening questions;
- you acknowledge what it has taken for her to share what is happening and you continue to demonstrate you believe what has been said;
- record all the information required by your job, but never in the form of hand-held records;
- the client is not pressurised into doing something or agreeing to action that she is uncomfortable with, as only she will know the length to which her abuser will go to hurt, punish, control or find her. This includes not being critical if a woman is unable to resolve the situation quickly; and
- her confidence is built up by acknowledging the steps she has taken already.

Appendix 8: Further reading

Life Transitions
- Gottman, J. M. & Schwartz Gottman, J. (2007). *And baby makes three: The six-step plan for preserving marital intimacy and rekindling romance after baby arrives.* Crown: New York.
- Jordan, P. L., Stanley, S. M. & Markman, H. J. (2001). *Becoming Parents: How to strengthen your marriage as your family grows.* San Francisco: Jossey-Bass.
- Mansfield, P. (2005). *Relationships Today: Transition to Parenthood.* Available from http://www.oneplusone.org.uk/Publications/InformationSheets/TheTransitionToParenthood.pdf

Attachment
- Bowlby, J. (1990). *A secure base: Parent-child attachment and healthy human development.* Basic Books.
- Clulow, C. (2001). *Adult attachment and couple psychotherapy. The 'secure base' in practice and research.* London: Brunner and Routledge.
- Johnson, S. M. & Whiffen, V. E. (2003). *Attachment processes in couple and family therapy.* New York: Guildford Press.

Helping
- Braun, D., Davis, H. & Mansfield, P. (2006). *How helping works: towards a shared model of process. London:* Parentline Plus.

What helps relationships work or fall apart?
- Gottman, J. & Silver, N. (2007) *Why marriages succeed or fail: and how to make yours last.* London: Bloomsbury.
- Markman, H., Stanley, S. M., & Blumberg, S. (2007). *Fighting for your marriage: Positive steps for preventing divorce and preserving a lasting love.* San Francisco: Jossey Bass.
- Glenn, F. (2007). *Growing together, or drifting apart? Children with disabilities and their parents' relationships.* London: One Plus One.

Partner choice / Relationship fit
- Pines, A. M. (1999). *Falling in love: Why we chose the lovers we choose.* New York: Routledge.
- One Plus One. *Predictors of relationship quality.* http://www.oneplusone.org.uk/Publications/InformationSheets/PredictorsOfRelationshipQuality.pdf

Better Partners, Better Parents
- Mansfield, P. (2005). Better partners, better parents. *Sexual and Relationship Therapy,* 20(3), 269-273.
- Gottman, J. M. (1997). *Raising an emotionally intelligent child: The heart of parenting.* London: Simon & Schuster.
- Parker, J., Simpson, J. & Rowe, D. (2004). *Raising happy children: What every child needs their parents to know.* London: Hodder Mobius.

- Jensen, A. & McKee, L. (2003). *Children and the challenging family: Between transformation and negotiation.* London: RoutledgeFalmer.

Parental conflict
- Reynolds, J. (2001). *Not in front of the children? How conflict between parents affects children.* London: One Plus One.
- Grych, J. & Fincham, F. D. (2001). *Interparental conflict and child development: Theory, research and application.* New York: Cambridge University Press.

Motivational Interviewing
- Miller, W. & Rollnick, S. (Eds) (2002). *Motivational interviewing: Preparing people for change.* New York: Guilford.
- Rollnick, S., Miller, W. & Butler, C. C. (2008). *Motivational interviewing in health care: Helping people change behavior.* New York: Guildford.

Transactional analysis
- Jones, V. & Stewart, I. (1987). *Transactional Analysis today – A new introduction to Transactional Analysis.* London: Lifespace.
- Stewart, I. (2007). *Transactional Analysis: Counselling in action.* London: Sage.
- De Board, R. (1997). *Counselling for toads: A psychological adventure.* London: Routledge.

Contemporary family life
- Almond, B. (2006). *The fragmenting family.* Oxford: Clarendon
- Lewis, J. E. (2001). *The end of marriage? Individualism and intimate relations.* Cheltenham: Elgar
- One Plus One (2004). *Relationships Today: Cohabitation.* Available from
  http://www.oneplusone.org.uk/Publications/InformationSheets/Cohabitation.pdf
- One Plus One. *Relationships Today: Changing Marriage.* Available from
  http://www.oneplusone.org.uk/Publications/InformationSheets/Changing%20marriage.pdf

Reflective Learning
- Burnard, P. (2002). *Learning human skills: An experiential and reflective guide for nurses and health care professionals.* Butterworth-Heinemann.

Supervision
- Proctor, B. (2008). *Group supervision: A guide to creative practice (2nd ed.) (Counselling Supervision series).* Sage.
- Hawkins, P., & Shohet, R. (2007). *Supervision in the helping professions (3rd ed.).* Open University Press.

Domestic violence
- Department of Health (2005). *Responding to domestic abuse: A handbook for health professionals.* London: HMSO.

Safeguarding children

- Hauser, S., Aleen, J. & Golden, E. (2006). *Out of the woods: Tales of resilient teens.* Cambridge, MA: Harvard University Press.
- Waldfogel, J. 2006). *What children need.* Harvard University Press: Cambridge, MA.

Counselling

- Burnard, P. (1999). *Counselling skills for health professionals* (3rd ed.). London: Chapman & Hall
- D'Ardenne, P., & Morrod, D. (2003). *The counselling of couples in healthcare settings.* London: Whurr.
- Levine, S. (2007). *Demystifying love: Plain talk for the mental health professional.* New York: Routledge.

References

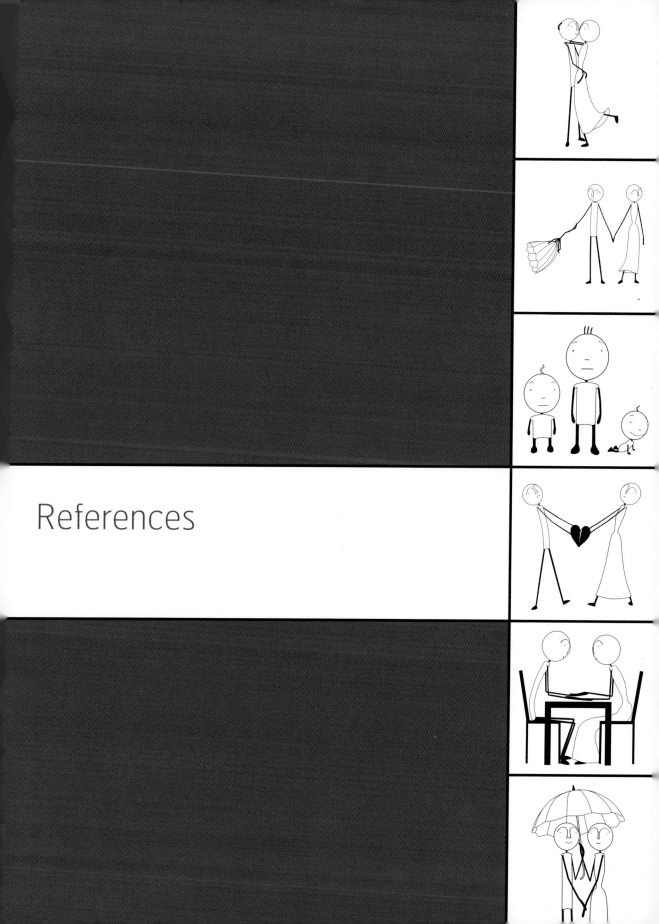

References

Adamsons, K., O'Brien, M. & Pasley, K. (2007). An ecological approach to father involvement in biological and stepfather families. *Fathering*, 5 (1), 29-147.

Adamsons, K. & Pasley, K. (2005). Coparenting following divorce and relationship dissolution. In. J. Harvey & M. Fine (Eds.), *The handbook of divorce and relationship dissolution* (pp.241-261). Mahwah, NJ: Lawrence Erlbaum Associates.

Afifi, W., Falato, W. & Weiner, J. (2001). Identity concerns following a severe relational transgression: The role of discovery method for the relational outcomes of infidelity. *Journal of Social and Personal Relationships,* 18 (2), 291-308.

Afifi, T. & Hamrick, K. (2005). Communication processes that promote risk and resiliency in postdivorce families. In J. Harvey and M. Fine (Eds.), *The handbook of divorce and relationship dissolution* (pp.435-456). Mahwah, NJ: Lawrence Erlbaum Associates.

Allen, I. & Bourke Dowling, S. (1998). *Teenage mothers: Decisions and outcomes.* London: Policy Studies Institute.

Allen, S. & Daly, K. (2004). *The effects of father involvement: A summary of the research evidence.* Ontario: Father Involvement Initiative.

Amato, P. (2000). The consequences of divorce for adults and children. *Journal of Marriage and the Family,* 62 (4), 1269-1287.

Amato, P. & Keith, B. (1991). Parental divorce and the well-being of children: A meta-analysis. *Psychological Bulletin,* 110 (1), 26-46.

Ambert, A. (2005). *Cohabitation and marriage: How are they related.* Ontario: The Vanier Institute of the Family.

Ayles, C. (2003). *Provision of training and resource materials to support community family workers in responding to couple relationship difficulties.* London: One Plus One.

Ayles, C. & Reynolds, J. (2001). *Identifying and managing patients' relationship problems in primary care: The perspective of health professionals and counsellors.* London: One Plus One.

Ballard, C. & Davies, R. (1996). Postnatal depression in fathers. *International Review of Psychiatry,* 8 (1), 65-71.

Banawan, S., O'Mahen, H., Beach, S. & Jackson, M. (2002). The empirical underpinnings of marital therapy for depression. In J. Harvey and A. Wenzel (Eds.) *A clinician's guide to maintaining and enhancing close relationships* (pp.133-155). Mahwah, NJ: Lawrence Erlbaum Associates.

Barlow, A., Burgoyne, C., Clery, E. & Smithson, J. (2008). Cohabitation and the law: Myths, money and the media. In A. Park et al., (Eds.) *British Social Attitudes. The 24th Report: 2007-2008 Edition* (pp.29-51). London: Sage.

Bauman, S. (2004). *Parents of children with mental retardation: Coping mechanisms and support needs.* Doctoral Dissertation. (Retrieved 18th October, 2006 from https://drum.umd.edu/dspace/bitstream/1903/1954/1/umi-umd-1903.pdf).

Beach, R., Kamen C. & Fincham, F. (2004). Marital dysfunction. In F. Andrasik (Ed.). *Comprehensive handbook of personality and psychopathology (CHOPP) Volume II: Adult psychopathology (Ch.28).* New York: Wiley.

Beck, A. (1967). *Depression: Clinical, experimental, and theoretical aspects.* New York: Hoeber Medical Division, Harper & Row.

Belsky, J. (1984). The determinants of parenting: A process model. *Child Development,* 55 (1), 83-96.

Belsky, J. & Kelly, L. (1994). *The transition to parenthood.* London: Vermillion.

Belsky, J., Lang, M. & Huston, T. (1986). Sex typing and division of labour as determinants of marital change across the transition to parenthood. *Journal of Personality and Social Psychology,* 50 (3), 517-522.

Berant, E., Mikulincer, M. & Florian, V. (2003). Marital satisfaction among mothers of infants with congenital heart disease: The contribution of illness severity, attachment style, and the coping process. *Anxiety, Stress & Coping,* 16 (4), 397-415.

Bergman K., Sarkar, P., O'Connor, T., Modi, N. & Glover, V. (2007). Maternal stress during pregnancy predicts cognitive ability and fearfulness in infancy. *Journal of the American Academy of Child and Adolescent Psychiatry,* 46 (11), 1454-1463.

Berrington, A., Stevenson, J., Ingham, J., with Borgoni, R ., Cobos Hernández, M. & Smith P. (2007). Consequences of teenage parenthood: Pathways which minimise the long-term negative impacts of teenage childbearing. *Department of Health Research Briefing,* 8, Jan 2007.

Biller, H. (1993). *Fathers and families: Paternal factors in child development.* Westport, CT: Auborn House.

Bodenmann, G. (2005). Dyadic coping and its significance for marital functioning. In T. Revenson, K. Kayser, and G. Bodenmann (Eds.) *Couples coping with stress: Emerging perspectives on dyadic coping* (pp.33-49). Washington DC: American Psychological Association.

Booth, A. & Edwards, J. (1992). Starting over: Why remarriages are more unstable. *Journal of Family Issues,* 13 (2), 179-194.

Bowman, M. & Ahrons, C. (1985). Impact of legal custody status on fathers' parenting postdivorce. *Journal of Marriage and the Family,* 47 (2), 481-487.

Bradbury, T. & Karney, B. (2004). Understanding and altering the longitudinal course of marriage. *Journal of Marriage and the Family,* 66 (4), 862-879.

Brannen, J. & Collard, J. (1982). *Marriages in trouble: The process of seeking help.* London: One Plus One.

Brook (2008). *Teenage conceptions: Statistics and trends.* (Retrieved July 2008 http://www.brook.org.uk/content/Fact2_TeenageConceptions.pdf)

Bruce M. & Kim, K. (1992). Differences in the effects of divorce on major depression in men and women. *American Journal of Psychiatry,* 149 (7), 914–917.

Buehler, C. & Ryan, C. (1994). Former-spouse relations and noncustodial father involvement during marital and family transitions: A closer look at remarriage following divorce. In K. Pasley and M. Ihinger-Tallman (Eds.), *Stepparenting: Issues in theory, research, and practice* (pp.127-150). Westport, CT: Greenwood.

Cabinet Office (2007). *Building on progress: Families – Policy review.* Prime Minister's Strategy Unit, Cabinet Office. London: Cabinet Office.

Cabinet Office (2008). *Think Family: Improving the life chances of children at risk. Social Exclusion Task Force, Cabinet Office.* London: Cabinet Office.

Cancerbackup & Relate (2008). Survey of cancer sufferers and their partners. (Retrieved July 2008) http://www.cancerbackup.org.uk/News/Mediacentre/Pressreleasesstatements/2008/32288181

Caplan, G. (1964). *Principles of preventive psychiatry.* New York: Basic Books.

Carlson, M. & Furstenberg, F. (2006). The prevalence and correlates of multipartnered fertility among urban US parents. *Journal of Marriage and the Family,* 68 (3), 718-732.

Carlson, M. & McLanahan, S. (2005). *Do good partners make good parents?* Centre for Research on Child Well-being. Working paper No. 02-16-FF. Princeton, NJ: Princeton University.

Carlson, M. & McLanahan, S. (2006). Strengthening unmarried families: Could enhancing couple relationships also improve parenting? *Social Service Review,* 80 (2), 297-321.

Carlson, M., McLanahan, S. & England, P. (2004). Union formation in fragile families. *Demography,* 41 (2), 237-262.

Office for National Statistics, General Register Office for Scotland, Northern Ireland Statistics and Research Agency (2001). *Census.* London: HMSO.

Centre for Social Justice (2008). *Breakthrough Britain: The next generation. A policy report from the Early Years Commission.* London: Centre for Social Justice.

Chase-Lansdale, P., Kiernan, K. & Friedman, R. (Eds.) (2004). *Human development across lives and generations: The potential for change.* New York: Cambridge University Press.

ChildLine (1998). *Unhappy families, unhappy children.* London: ChildLine.

Clulow, C. (Ed.) (2001a). *Adult attachment and couple psychotherapy.* London: Brunner-Routledge.

Clulow, C. (Ed.) (2001b). *Rethinking marriage, public and private perspectives.* London: Karnac Books.

Cobb, R., Davila, J. & Bradbury, T. (2001). Attachment security and marital satisfaction: The role of positive perceptions and social support. *Personality & Social Psychology Bulletin,* 27 (9), 1131-1143.

Coiro, M. & Emery, R. (1998). Do marriage problems affect fathering more than mothering? A quantitative and qualitative review. *Clinical Child and Family Psychology Review,* 1 (1), 23-40.

Coleman, L. & Glenn, F. (forthcoming - provisional title) *A review of the evidence on couple relationship breakdown.* London: One Plus One.

Coleman, M. & Ganong, L. (1985). Remarriage myths: Implications for the helping professions. *Journal of Counselling and Development,* 64 (1), 116-120.

Colman, W. (1995). *Understanding affairs.* Paper presented at One Plus One annual conference, 'The State of Affairs', May, 1995.

Conger, R., Conger, K., Elder, G., Lonrenz, F., Simons, R. & Whitbeck, L. (1992). A family process model of economic hardship and adjustment of early adolescent boys. *Child Development,* 63 (3), 526-541.

Conger, R., Elder, G., Lorenz, E., Conger, K., Simons, R., Whitbeck, L., Huck, S. & Melby, J. (1990). Linking economic hardship to marital quality and instability. *Journal of Marriage and the Family,* 52 (3), 643-656.

Conger, R., Rueter, M. & Elder, G. Jr. (2002). Couple resilience to economic pressure. In P. Boss (Ed.), *Family stress: Classic and contemporary readings* (pp.292-319). Thousand Oaks, CA: Sage Publications.

Contact a Family (2004). *No time for us: Relationships between parents who have a disabled child: A survey of over 2000 parents in the UK.* London: Contact a Family.

Cooper, C., McLanan, S., Meadows, S. & Brooks-Gunn, J. (2007). *Family structure transitions and maternal parenting stress.* Center for Research on Child Wellbeing, Working Paper 2007-16-FF. Princeton NJ. Princeton University.

Cooper, P., Murray, L., Wilson, A., & Romaniuk, H. (2003). Controlled trial of the short and long term effects of psychological treatment of postpartum depression. *The British Journal of Psychiatry,* 182 (5), 420-429.

Corney, R. (1990). A survey of professional help sought by patients for psychosocial problems. *British Journal of General Practice,* 40 (338), 365-368.

Corney, R. (1998). *Evaluation of the brief encounters training course.* London: University of Greenwich.

Corney, R. (2005). *The impact of breast cancer on couple satisfaction and their relationship quality: A review of the literature.* London: One Plus One.

Corney, R., Ayles, C. & Negreira, C. (2006). *Parent conflict: Reducing the fallout for children and adults. Report outlining the stages of the project and focusing on evaluation.* London: One Plus One.

Council of Europe (2002). *Recommendation of the Committee of Ministers to member States on the protection of women against violence.* Adopted on 30 April 2002; and Explanatory Memorandum. Strasbourg, France: Council of Europe.

Cowan, C. & Cowan, P. (2000). *When partners become parents: The big life change for couples.* Mahwah, NJ: Lawrence Erlbaum Associates.

Cowan, P. & Cowan, C., (2003). Normative family transitions, normal family process, and health child development. In F. Walsh (Ed.). *Normal family processes,* 3rd Edition (pp.424-459). New York: The Guilford Press.

Cowan, P., Cowan, C., Ablow, J., Johnson, V. & Measelle, J. (2005). *The family context of parenting in children's adaptation to elementary school.* Mahwah, NJ: Lawrence Erlbaum Associates.

Cowan, C., Cowan, P., Heming, G. & Miller N. (1991). Becoming a family: Marriage, parenting and child development. In P. Cowan and M. Hetherington (Eds.) *Family Transitions* (pp.79-109). New York: Hillsdale.

Cox, M., Paley, B., Payne, C. & Burchinal, M. (1999). The transition to parenthood: Marital conflict and withdrawal and parent-infant interactions. In M. Cox and J. Brooks-Gunn (Eds.) *Conflict and cohesion in families: Causes and consequences* (pp.87-104). Mahwah, NJ: Erlbaum.

Coyne, J., Ellard, J. & Smith, D. (1990). Social support, interdependence, and the dilemmas of helping. In B. Sarason, I. Sarason and G. Pierce (Eds.) *Social Support: An interactional view* (pp.129-149). New York: John Wiley.

CPHVA (2005). Clinical Effectiveness. *Information Briefing,* 18.

Crockenberg, S. (1987). Predictors and correlates of anger towards and punitive control of toddlers by adolescent mothers. *Child Development,* 58 (4), 964-975.

Cummings, E. M. & O'Reilly, A. (1997). Fathers in family context: Effects of marital quality on child adjustment. In M. E. Lamb, (Ed.), *The role of the father in child development.* 3rd Edition (pp.49-65). New York: John Wiley.

Cutrona, C. (1996). *Social support in couples.* CA: Sage.

Cutrona, C. (2004). A psychological perspective: Marriage and the social provisions of relationships. *Journal of Marriage and the Family.* 66 (4), 992-999.

d'Ardenne, P. & Morrod, D., (2003). *The counselling of couples in healthcare settings: A handbook for clinicians.* London: Whurr Publishers.

Dadds, M., Schwartz, S. & Sanders, M. (1987). Marital discord and treatment outcome in behavioural treatment of child behaviour problems. *Journal of Consulting and Clinical Psychology,* 55 (3), 396-403.

Department for Education and Skills (2003). *Every Child Matters.* London: Department for Education and Skills.

Department for Education and Skills (2005). *Common Core of Skills and Knowledge for the Children's Workforce.* London: HMSO.

Department for Children, Schools and Families (2007). *Every Parent Matters.* London: Department for Children, Skills and Families.

Department for Children, Schools and Families (2007). *The Children's Plan: Building brighter futures.* London: Department for Children, School and Families.

Department of Health (2005). *Responding to domestic abuse: A handbook for professionals.* London: Department of Health.

Department of Health (2006). *Modernising nursing careers: Setting the direction.* London: Department of Health.

Department of Health (2007). *Facing the future: A review of the role of health visitors.* London: Department of Health.

Department of Health & Department for Education and Skills (2004). *National Service Framework for Children, Young People and Maternity Services.* London: Department of Health.

Department of Health & Department for Education and Skills (2005). *Sure Start Children's Centres Practice Guidance.* London: Department for Education and Skills.

Department of Health & Department for Children, Schools and Families (2008). *Child Health Promotion Programme. Pregnancy and the first five years of life.* London: Department of Health.

DeVito, C. & Hopkins, J. (2001). Attachment, parenting, and marital dissatisfaction as predictors of disruptive behaviour in preschoolers. *Development and Psychopathology,* 13 (2), 215-231.

Doherty, W., Kouneski, E. & Erickson, M. (1998). Responsible fathering: An overview and conceptual framework. *Journal of Marriage and the Family,* 60 (22), 277-292.

Dolan, S. & Nathan, P. (2002). When one marital partner is an alcoholic. In J. Harvey and A. Wenzel (Eds.) *A clinician's guide to maintaining and enhancing close relationships* (pp.215-229). Mahwah, NJ: Erlbaum.

Driver J., Tabares, A., Shapiro A., Young Nahm, E. & Gottman, J. (2003). Interaction patterns in marital success and failure: Gottman Laboratory Studies. In F. Walsh (Ed.) *Normal family processes. Third Edition. Growing diversity and complexity* (pp.493-513). New York: The Guilford Press.

Duck, S. & Wood J. (2005). What goes up may come down: Sex and gendered patterns in relational dissolution. In J. Harvey & M. Fine (Eds.), *The handbook of divorce and relationship dissolution* (pp.169-187). Mahwah, NJ: Lawrence Erlbaum Associates.

Duncan, S. & Smith, D. (2004). In *Seven ages of man and woman*. Swindon: Economic and Social Research Council.

Dunn, J. & Deater-Deckard, K. (2001). *Children's views of their changing families*. Findings No. 931. York: Joseph Rowntree Foundation.

Easterbrooks, M. & Emde, R. (1988). Parenting in context: Systemic thinking about parental conflict and its influence on children. *Journal of Consulting and Clinical Psychology*, 60 (6), 909-912.

Edin, K., Kefalas, M. & Reed, J. (2004). A peek inside the black box: What marriage means for poor unmarried parents. *Journal of Marriage and the Family*, 66 (4), 1007-1014.

Erickson, R. (1993). Reconceptualizing family work: The effect of emotion work on perceptions of marital quality. *Journal of Marriage and the Family*, 55 (4), 888-900.

Feinberg, M. (2002). Coparenting and the transition to parenthood: A framework for prevention. *Clinical Child and Family Psychology Review*, 5 (3), 173-195.

Feinberg, M. & Kan, M. (2008). Establishing family foundations: Intervention effects on coparenting, parent/infant well-being, and parent-child relations. *Journal of Family Psychology*, 22 (2), 253-263.

Ferri, E. & Smith, K. (1998). *Step-parenting in the 1990s*. London: Family Policy Studies Centre.

Fincham, F. (2003). Marital conflict: Correlates, structure, and context. *Current Directions in Psychological Science*, 12 (1), 23-27.

Fincham, F. & Hall, H. (2005) Parenting and the marital relationship. In T. Luster and L. Okagaki (Eds.) *Parenting: An ecological perspective. 2nd Edition* (pp.205-234). Mahwah, NJ: Lawrence Erlbaum Associates.

Fincham, F., Beach, S., Harold, G. & Osborne, L. (1997). Marital satisfaction and depression: Different causal relationships for men and women? *Psychological Science*, 8 (5), 351-357.

Floyd, F., Klotz Daugherty, M., Fitzgerald, H., Cranford, J. & Zucker, R. (2006). Marital interaction in alcoholic and nonalcoholic couples: Alcoholic subtype variations and wives' alcoholism status, *Abnormal Psychology*, 115 (1), 121–130.

Ganong, L. & Coleman, M. (2004). *Stepfamily relationships: Development, dynamics and interventions*. New York: Kluwer Academic/Plenum Publishers.

Ganong, L., Coleman, M. & Weaver, S. (2002). Relationship maintenance and enhancement in stepfamilies: Clinical applications. In J. Harvey and A. Wenzel (Eds.) *A clinician's guide to maintaining and enhancing close relationships* (pp.105-129). Mahwah, NJ: Erlbaum.

Gee, C. & Rhodes, J. (1999). Postpartum transitions in adolescent mothers' romantic and maternal relationships. *Merrill-Palmer Quarterly*, 45 (3), 512-532.

Gee, C. & Rhodes, J. (2003). Adolescent mothers' relationships with their children's biological fathers: Social support, social strain, and relationship continuity. *Journal of Family Psychology*, 17 (3), 370–383.

Gjerdingen, D., Froberg, D. & Fontaine, P. (1991). The effects of social support on women's health during pregnancy, labor, and delivery, and the postpartum period. *Family Medicine*, 23 (5), 370-375.

Glenn, F. (2007). *Growing together or drifting apart? Children with disabilities and their parents' relationships*. London: One Plus One.

Golombok, S. & Tasker, F. (1996). Do parents influence the sexual orientation of their children? Findings from a longitudinal study of lesbian families. *Developmental Psychology*, 32 (1), 3–11.

Gordon, K., Baucom, D. & Snyder, D. (2004). An integrative intervention for promoting recovery from extramarital affairs. *Journal of Marital and Family Therapy*, 30 (2), 213–231.

Gottman, J. (1994a). *The seven principles for making marriage work. What predicts divorce? The relationship between marital processes and marital outcomes.* Hillsdale, NJ: Erlbaum.

Gottman, J. (1994b). *What predicts divorce? The relationship between marital processes and marital outcomes.* Hillsdale, NJ: Erlbaum.

Gottman, J., Ryan, I., Carrere, S. & Erley, A. (2002). Toward a scientifically based marital therapy. In H. Liddle, D. Santisteban, R. Levant & J. Bray (Eds.), *Family psychology: Science-based interventions* (pp.147-174). Washington, DC: American Psychological Association.

Gottman, J., Levenson, R., Gross, J., Frederickson, B., McCoy, K., Rosenthal, L., Ruef, A. & Yoshimoto, D. (2003). Correlates of gay and lesbian couples' relationship satisfaction and relationship dissolution. *Journal of Homosexuality*, 45 (1), 65-91.

Grych, J. (2002). Marital relationships and parenting. In M. Bornstein (Ed.), *Handbook of parenting: Vol. 4. Social conditions and applied parenting* (pp.203-225). Mahwah, NJ: Lawrence Erlbaum Assocaties.

Gutteridge, R. (2003). *Enduring relationships: The evolution of long-lasting marriages.* Keele University, PhD Dissertation.

Hagedoorn, M., Sanderman, R., Bolks, H. & Tuinstra, J. (2008). Distress in couples coping with cancer: A meta-analysis and critical review of role and gender effects. *Psychological Bulletin.* 134 (1), 1–30.

Halford, W. & Osgarby, S. (1993). Alcohol abuse in clients presenting with marital problems. *Journal of Family Psychology*, 6 (3), 1-11.

Hall, J. & Fincham, F. (2005). Relationship dissolution following infidelity In: M. Fine and J. Harvey (Eds.), *The handbook of divorce and relationship dissolution* (pp.153-168). Mahwah, NJ: Lawrence Erlbaum Associates.

Harold, G. (2001). What matters about conflict? In J. Reynolds (Ed.) *Not in front of the children? How conflict between parents affects children.* London: One Plus One.

Harold, G., Aitken, J. & Shelton, K. (2007). Inter-parental conflict and children's academic attainment: A longitudinal analysis. *Journal of Child Psychology and Psychiatry*, 48 (12), 1223-1232.

Harris, T., Brown, G. & Robinson, R. (1999). Befriending as an intervention for chronic depression among women in an inner city. 2: Role of fresh-start experiences and baseline psychosocial factors in remission from depression. *British Journal of Psychiatry*, 174 (3), 225-232.

Harrison, K. & Allan, G. (2001). Sexual affairs and marriage. *Bulletin Plus*, 5 (1), 4-5.

Hawthorne, J., Jessop, J., Pryor, J. & Richards, M. (2003). *Supporting children through family change: A review of interventions and services for children of divorcing and separating parents.* Findings No. 323. York: Joseph Rowntree Foundation.

Heron, J., O'Connor, T., Evans, J., Golding, J. & Glover, V. (2004). The course of anxiety and depression through pregnancy and the postpartum in a community sample. *Journal of Affective Disorders,* 80 (1), 65–73.

Herzog, M., Umana-Taylor, A., Madden-Derdich, D. & Leonard, S. (2007). Adolescent mothers' perceptions of fathers' parental involvement: Satisfaction and desire for involvement. *Family Relations,* 56 (3), 244-257.

Hetherington, E.M. (2003). Intimate pathways: Changing patterns in close personal relationships across time. *Family Relations,* 52 (4), 318-331.

HM Treasury (2007). *Aiming high: Supporting families.* London: HM Treasury.

Home Office (2003). *Safety and justice: The government's proposals on domestic violence.* London: Home Office.

Hooley, J. & Teasdale, J. (1989). Predictors of relapse in unipolar depressives: Expressed emotion, marital distress, and perceived criticism. *Journal of Abnormal Psychology,* 98 (3), 229-235.

Hore, B. (1971). Life events and alcoholic relapse. *British Journal of Addiction,* 66 (2), 83-88.

Huston, T. & Melz, H. (2004). The case for (promoting) marriage: The devil is in the details. *Journal of Marriage and the Family,* 66 (4), 943-958.

Jacob, T., Ritchey, D., Cvitkovic, J. & Blane H. (1981). Communication styles of alcoholic and non-alcoholic families when drinking and not drinking. *Journal of Studies on Alcohol,* 42, 466–482.

Joesch, J. & Smith, K. (1997). Children's health and their mother's risk of divorce or separation. *Social Biology,* 44 (3-4), 159-169.

Johnson, A., Mercer, C., Erens, B., Copas, A., McManus, S., Wellings, K., Fenton, K., Korovessis, C., Macdowall, W., Nanchaha, I. K., Purdon, S. & Field, J. (2001). Sexual behaviour in Britain: Partnerships, practices and HIV risk behaviours. *The Lancet,* 358 (9296), 1835-1842.

Johnson, M. & Ferraro, J. (2000) Research on domestic violence in the 1990s: Making distinctions. *Journal of Marriage and the Family,* 62 (4), 948-963.

Joiner, T., Jr. & Metalsky, G. (1995). A prospective test of an integrative interpersonal theory of depression: A naturalistic study of college roommates. *Journal of Personality and Social Psychology,* 69 (4), 778-788.

Jordan, P. (1990). Laboring for relevance: Expectant and new fatherhood. *Nursing Research,* 39 (1), 11-16.

Kagan, J., Reznick, J. & Snidman, N. (1987). The physiology and psychology of behavioral inhibition in children. *Child Development,* 58 (6), 1459–1473.

Kalmijn, M. (1999). Father involvement in childrearing and the perceived stability of marriage. *Journal of Marriage and the Family,* 61 (2), 409-421.

Karney, B. & Bradbury, T. (1995). The longitudinal course of marital quality and stability: A review of theory, method, and research. *Psychological Bulletin,* 118 (1), 3–34.

Karney, B. & Bradbury, T. (1997). Neuroticism, marital interaction, and the trajectory of marital satisfaction. *Journal of Personality and Social Psychology,* 72 (5), 1075–1092.

Karney, B., Story, L. & Bradbury, T. (2003). *Marriages in context: Interactions between chronic and acute stress among newlyweds.* Presented at the International Meeting on the Developmental Course of Couples Coping with Stress, October 12-14, 2002, Boston College, Chestnut Hill, MA.

Katz, J. (2001). Self-verification theory: Expanding current conceptualizations of the link between marital distress and depression. In S. Beach (Ed.), *Marital and family processes in depression: A scientific foundation for clinical practice* (pp.111-127). Washington, DC: American Psychological Association.

Kayser, K. & Rao, S. (2005). Process of disaffection in relationship breakdown. In J. Harvey and M. Fine (Eds.), *The handbook of divorce and relationship dissolution* (pp.201-221). Mahwah, N: Lawrence Erlbaum Associates.

Kessler, R., Magee, W. & Nelson, C. (1996). Analysis of psychosocial stress. In H.B. Kaplan (Ed.) *Psychosocial stress: Perspectives on structure, theory, life-course, and methods.* San Diego, CA: Academic Press.

Kluwer. E., Heesink. J. & Vliert, E. (1997). The marital dynamics of conflict over the division of labour. *Journal of Marriage and the Family,* 59 (3), 635-653.

Kovacs, L., (1988). Couple therapy: An integrated and developmental family systems model. *Family Therapy,* 15(2), 133-155.

Krishnakumar, A. & Buehler, C. (2000). Interparental conflict and parenting behaviors: A meta-analytic review. *Family Relations,* 49 (1), 25-44.

Kurdek, L. (1998). Relationship outcomes and their predictors: Longitudinal evidence from heterosexual married, gay cohabiting and lesbian cohabiting couples. *Journal of Marriage and the Family,* 60 (3), 553-568.

Kurdek, L. (2001). Differences between heterosexual-nonparent couples and gay, lesbian, and heterosexual-parent couples. *Journal of Family Issues,* 22 (6), 727–754.

Kurdek, L. (2004a). Gay men and lesbians: The family context. In M. Coleman & L.H. Ganong (Eds.), *Handbook of contemporary families: Considering the past, contemplating the future* (pp. 96–115). Thousand Oaks, CA: Sage.

Kurdek, L. (2004b). Are gay and lesbian cohabiting couples really different from heterosexual married couples? *Journal of Marriage and the Family,* 66 (4), 880–900.

Laird, J. (2003). Lesbian and gay families. In F. Walsh (Ed.) *Normal family processes. 3rd Edition. Growing diversity and complexity.* NY: The Guilford Press.

Lane, A., Wilcoxon, S. & Cecil, J. (1988). Family-of-origin experiences and the transition to parenthood: Considerations for marital and family therapists. *Family Therapy,* 15 (1), 23–29.

Larsen, K. & O'Hara, M. (2002). The effects of postpartum depression on close relationships. In J. Harvey and A. Wenzel (Eds.) *A clinician's guide to maintaining and enhancing close relationships* (pp.157-176). Mahwah, NJ: Lawrence Erlbaum Associates.

Larson, N., Hussey, J., Gilmore, M. & Gilchrist, L. (1996). What about Dad? Fathers of children born to schoolmothers. *Families in Society: The Journal of Contemporary Human Services,* May, 279–289.

Lawrence, E., Rothman, A., Cobb, R., Rothman, M. & Bradbury, T. (2008). Marital satisfaction across the transition to parenthood. *Journal of Family Psychology,* 22 (1), 41-50.

Levy-Schiff, R. (1994). Individual and contextual correlates of marital change across the transition to parenthood. *Developmental Psychology,* 30 (4), 591-601.

Lindahl, M., Clements, M. & Markman, H. (1997). Predicting marital and parent functioning in dyads and triads: A longitudinal investigation of marital processes. *Journal of Family Psychology,* 11 (2), 139-151.

Luster, T. & Haddow, J. (2005). Adolescent mother and their children: An ecological perspective. In T. Luster & L. Okagaki (2002). *Parenting: An ecological perspective. 2nd Edition* (pp.73-101). Mahwah, NJ: Lawrence Erlbaum Associates.

Lyons, A. (1992). Husbands and wives: The mysterious choice. In. S. Ruszczynski (Ed.) *Psychotherapy with couples*. London: Karnac Books.

Manning, W. & Smock, P. (1999). New families and nonresident father-child visitation. *Social Forces*, 78 (1), 87-116.

Margolin, G., Gordis, E. & John, R. (2001). Coparenting: A link between marital conflict and parenting in two-parent families. *Journal of Family Psychology*, 15 (1), 3-21.

Masheter, C. (1991). Postdivorce relationships between ex-spouses: The role of attachment and interpersonal conflict. *Journal of Marriage and the Family*, 53 (1), 103-110.

Matthews, L. Conger, R. & Wickrama, K. (1996). Work-family conflict and marital quality: Mediating processes. *Social Psychology Quarterly*, 59 (1), 62-79.

McAllister, F. (1995). *Marital breakdown and the health of the nation*. 2nd Edition. London: One Plus One.

McLanahan, S. & Carlson, M. (2002). Welfare reform, fertility, and father involvement. *The Future of Our Children*, 12 (1), 147–163.

Mead, E. (2002). Marital distress, co-occurring depression and marital therapy: A review. *Journal of Marital and Family Therapy*, 28, (3), 299-314.

Mencap (2001). *No ordinary life. The support needs of families caring for children and adults with profound and multiple learning disabilities*. Mencap: London.

Mills, D. (1984). A model for stepfamily development. *Family Relations*, 33, 365-372.

Moran, P., Ghate, D. & Van der Merwe, A. (2004). *What works in parenting support? A review of the international evidence*. Research Report 574. London: Department for Education and Skills.

Morrison, V. & Bennett, P. (2006). *An introduction to health psychology*. Pearson Education Limited: Essex.

Morrod, D. & Munro, S. (2006). *My mum and dad argue a lot. Parent conflict: Avoiding the fallout for children and adults*. London: One Plus One.

Murphy, C. & O'Farrel, T. (1997). Couple communication patterns of maritally aggressive and non-aggressive male alcoholics. *Journal of Studies on Alcohol*, 58 (1), 83-90.

Murray, L. & Cooper, P. (1997). *Postpartum depression and child development*. New York: The Guilford Press.

National Family and Parenting Institute (2000). *Teenagers' attitude to parenting: A survey of young people's experiences of being parented, and their views on how to bring up children*. (MORI survey). London: NFPI.

National Statistics (2006a). *Birth statistics: Review of the Registrar General on births and patterns of family building in England and Wales, 2005. Series FM1, no 34*. London: The Stationery Office.

National Statistics (2006b). *Social Trends 36*. London: The Stationery Office.

National Statistics (2007a). *Birth statistics: Review of the Registrar General on births and patterns of family building in England and Wales, 2006. Series FM1, no 35*. London: The Stationery Office.

National Statistics (2007b). *Social Trends 37.* London: The Stationery Office.

National Statistics (2008a). *Marriage, divorce and adoption statistics: Review of the Registrar General on marriages and divorces in 2005 and adoptions in 2006, in England and Wales. Series FM2, no 33.* London: The Stationery Office.

National Statistics (2008b). *Social Trends 38.* London: The Stationery Office.

Neff, L. & Karney, B. (2004). How does context affect intimate relationships? Linking external stress and cognitive processes within marriage. *Journal of Personality and Social Psychology Bulletin,* 30 (2), 134-148.

Nelson, G. & Beach, S. (1990). Sequential interaction in depression: Effects of depressive behavior on spousal aggression. *Behavior Therapy,* 21 (2), 167-182.

Noel, N., McCrady, B., Stout, R. & Fisher-Nelson, H. (1991). Gender differences in marital functioning of male and female alcoholics. *Family Dynamics of Addiction Quarterly,* 1, 31-38.

Nolan, P., Skinstad, A. & Dolan S. (2001). The alcohol-related disorders: Psychopathology, diagnosis, etiology, and treatment. In P. Sutker and H. Adams (Eds.) *Comprehensive handbook of psychopathology. 3rd Edition.* New York: Plenum.

O'Connor, T.G., Heron, J., Golding, J., Beveridge, M. & Glover, V. (2002). Maternal antenatal anxiety and children's behavioral/emotional problems at 4 years. Report from the Avon Longitudinal Study of Parents and Children. *British Journal of Psychiatry,* 180 (1), 502–508.

O'Connor, T., Heron, J., Golding, J. & Glover, V. (2003). Maternal antenatal anxiety and behavioral/ emotional problems in children: A test of a programming hypothesis. *Journal of Child Psychology and Psychiatry,* 44 (7), 1025–1036.

O'Connor, E., McCabe, M. & Firth L. (2008). The impact of neurological illness on marital relationships. *Journal of Sexual and Marital Therapy,* 34 (2), 115-32.

O'Farrell, T. & Choquette, K. (1991). Marital violence in the year before and after spouse-involved alcoholism treatment. *Family Dynamics of Addiction Quarterly,* 1 (1), 32-40.

O'Farrell, T. & Murphy, C. (1995). Marital violence before and after alcoholism treatment. *Journal of Consulting and Clinical Psychology,* 63 (2), 256 -262.

O'Hara, M., Zekoski, E., Philipps, L. & Wright, E. (1990). A controlled prospective study of postpartum mood disorders: Comparisons of childbearing and nonchildbearing women. *Journal of Abnormal Psychology,* 99 (1), 3-15.

Oakley, A., Rigby, S. & Hickey, D. (1994). Life stress and class inequality: Explaining the health of women and children. *European Journal of Public Health,* 4 (2), 81-91.

Olson, M., Candyce, R., Higgins-Kessler, M. & Miller, R. (2002). Emotional processes following disclosure of an extramarital affair. *Journal of Marital and Family Therapy,* 28 (4), 423–434.

One Plus One (2006). *Fragile families and child well-being.* The Edith Dominian Memorial Lecture, 2006. London: One Plus One.

Osborne, C. & McLanahan, S. (2007). Partnership instability and child well-being. *Journal of Marriage and the Family,* 69 (5), 1065-1083.

Oswald, R. & Clausell, E. (2005). Same sex relationships and their dissolution. In M. Fine and J. Harvey, (Eds.) *Handbook of divorce and relationship dissolution.* Mahwah, NJ: Lawrence Erlbaum Associates.

Paisley, K., Futris, T. & Skinner, M. (2002). Effects of commitment and psychological centrality on fathering. *Journal of Marriage and the Family,* 64 (1), 130-138.

Parke, M. (2004). *Who are fragile families and what do we know about them?* Couples and Marriage Series, January 2004, Policy Brief No. 4. Center for Law and Social Policy (CLASP).

Parker, R. (2002) *Why marriages last: A discussion of the literature.* Research Paper No. 28, July. Australian Institute of Family Studies.

Pasley, K., Rhoden, J., Visher, E. & Visher, J. (1996). Successful stepfamily therapy: Clients' perspectives. *Journal of Marital and Family Therapy,* 22 (3), 319-333.

Patterson, C. (2000). Family relationships of lesbians and gay men. *Journal of Marriage and the Family,* 62 (4), 1052–1069.

Patterson, C. (2006). Children of lesbian and gay parents. *Current Directions in Psychological Science,* 15 (5), 241-244.

Perren, S., Von Wyl, A., Burgin, D., Simoni, H. & Von Klitzing, K. (2005) Intergenerational transmission of marital quality across the transition to parenthood. *Family Process,* 44 (4), 441-459.

Pike, A., Coldwell, J. & Dunn, J. (2006). *Family relationships in middle childhood.* London: NCB for JRF.

Proctor, B. & Inskipp, F. (1993). *Skills for supervising and being supervised. Audiotape and Booklets.* Tape 1: Being supervised. St Leonards on Sea: Alexia Publications.

Pryor, J. (2001). Partnership quality and children's well-being after separation. In. J. Reynolds (Ed.) *Not in front of the children? How conflict between parents affects children* (pp.23-28). London: One Plus One.

Pryor, J. & Rodgers, B. (2001). *Children in changing families: Life after parental separation.* Oxford: Blackwell.

Quinton, D. (2004) *Supporting parents: Messages from research.* London: Jessica Kingsley Publishers.

Quinton, D., Pollock, S. & Golding, J. (2002). *The transition to fatherhood in young men: Influences on commitment.* Report to the ESRC L134251018.

Rapoport, R., Rapoport, R. & Streilitz, Z. (1977). *Mothers, fathers and society: Towards new alliances.* New York: Basic Books.

Raskin, V., Richman J. & Gaines, C. (1990). Patterns in depressive symptoms in expectant and new parents. *American Journal of Psychiatry,* 147 (5), 658-660.

Relate (2008). *Relate at 70.* (Retrieved August 2008 www.relate.org.uk).

Reynolds, J. (2001). *Not in front of the children? How conflict between parents affects children.* London: One Plus One.

Reynolds, J. (2002). *An exploratory study of the effects of training community mothers to respond to couple relationship difficulties.* London: One Plus One.

Reynolds, J., Ayles, C. & Tucker, V. (2002). *Implementing the primary care for couples guide: Report of a pilot study.* London: One Plus One.

Riessman, C. (1990). *Divorce talk: Women and men make sense of personal relationships.* New Brunswick, NJ: Rutgers University Press.

Ristock, J. & Timbang, N. (2005). *Relationship violence in Lesbian/Gay/Bisexual/ Transgender/Queer [LGBTQ] Communities: Moving beyond a gender-based framework.* Violence Against Women Online Resources. (Retrieved August 2008 http://www.vawnet.org/).

Robinson, E. & Parker, R. (2008). Prevention and early intervention in strengthening families and relationships: Challenges and implications. Australian Family Relationships Clearinghouse. *Issues, 2.* (Retrieved August 2008 http://www.aifs.gov.au/afrc/pubs/issues2/issues2.pdf)

Rodgers, B. & Pryor, J. (1998). *Divorce and separation: The outcomes for children.* York: Joseph Rowntree Foundation.

Rollie, S. & Duck, S. (2005). Divorce and dissolution of romantic relationships: Stage models and their limitations. In J. Harvey and M. Fine (Eds.), *The handbook of divorce and relationship dissolution* (pp.223-239). Mahwah, NJ: Lawrence Erlbaum Associates.

Rollie, S., Miller, W. & Butler, C. (2008) *Motivational interviewing in health care.* New York: Guilford Press.

Rubin, L. (1985) *Just friends: The role of friendship in our lives.* New York: Harper and Row.

Rusch, N. & Corrigan, P. (2002). Motivational Interviewing to improve insight and treatment adherence in schizophrenia. *Journal of Psychiatry,* Vol. 26 (1), 23-32.

Rydström, I., Dalheim-Englund, A., Segesten, K. & Rasmussen, B. (2004). Relations governed by uncertainty: Part of life of families of a child with Asthma. *Journal of Pediatric Nursing,* 19 (2), 85-94.

Schachner, D., Shaver, P. & Mikulincer, M. (2006). Adult attachment theory, psychodynamics, and couple relationships: An overview. In S. Johnson and V. Whiffen (Eds.), *Attachment processes in couple and family therapy* (pp.18-42). New York: Guilford Press.

Schmaling, K. & Jacobson, N. (1990). Marital interaction and depression. *Journal of Abnormal Psychology,* 99 (3), 229-236.

Schulz, M., Cowan, P., Cowan, C. & Brennan, R. (2004). Coming home upset: Gender, marital satisfaction, and the daily spillover of workday experience into couple interactions. *Journal of Family Psychology,* 18 (1), 250–263.

Silverstein, J. (1998). Countertransference in marital therapy for infidelity. *Journal of Sex and Marital Therapy,* 24 (4), 293-301.

Simms, L. (2002). The application of attachment theory to individual behaviour and functioning in close relationships: Theory, research, and practical applications. In J. Harvey and A. Wenzel (Eds.), *A clinician's guide to maintaining and enhancing close relationships* (pp.63-80). Mahwah, NJ: Lawrence Erlbaum Associates.

Simons, J. (1999). Theories of disenchantment. In Simons, J. (Ed.), High Divorce Rates: *The state of the evidence on reasons and remedies.* Volume 2. London: Lord Chancellor's Department.

Simons, J., Reynolds, J., Morison, L. & Mannion, J. (2003). How the health visitor can help when problems between parents add to postnatal depression. *Journal of Advanced Nursing,* 44 (4), 400-411.

Simons, R., Beaman, J., Conger, R. & Chao, W. (1993). Childhood experiences, conceptions of parenting, and attitudes of spouse as determinants of parental behaviour. *Journal of Marriage and the Family,* 55 (1), 91.

Spanier, G., Rovine, M. & Belsky, J. (1983). Stability and change in marriage across the transition to parenthood. *Journal of Marriage and the Family,* 42 (4), 825-839.

Spector, A. (2006). Fatherhood and depression: A review of risks, effects and clinical application. *Issues in Mental Health Nursing,* 27 (8), 867-883.

Stanko, E. (2000). *The day to count: A snapshot of the impact of domestic violence in the UK.* Criminal Justice 1:2.

Stewart-Brown, S. & Shaw, R. (2004). The roots of social capital: Relationships in the home during childhood and health in later life. In A. Morgan and C. Swann (Eds.), *Social capital for health: Issues of definition, measurement and links to health* (p158-185). London: Health Development Agency.

Storey, A., Walsh, C., Quinton, R. & Wynne-Edwards, K. (2000). Hormonal correlates of paternal responsiveness in new and expectant fathers. *Evolution and Human Behavior,* 21 (2), 79-95.

Suh, E., Moskowitz, D., Fournier, M. & Zurroff, D. (2004). Gender and relationships: Influences on agentic and communal behaviours. *Personal Relationships,* 11 (1), 41-59.

Sure Start. (2002). *Working with diversity.* London: Department for Education and Skills.

Swann, C., Bowe, K., McCormick, G. & Kosmin, M. (2003). *Teenage pregnancy and parenthood: A review of reviews. Evidence briefing. 1st Edition.* London: NHS Health Development Agency.

Talge, N., Neal C. & Glover V. (2007). Antenatal maternal stress and long-term effects on child neurodevelopment: How and why? *Journal of Child Psychology and Psychiatry,* 48 (3/4), 245–261.

Tesser, A. & Beach, S. (1998). Life events, relationship quality, and depression: An investigation of judgment discontinuity in vivo. *Journal of Personality and Social Psychology,* 74 (1), 36-52.

Thompson, M. & Peebles-Wilkins, W. (1992). The impact of formal, informal and societal support networks on the psychological well-being of black adolescent mothers. *Social Work,* 37 (4), 322-328.

Tower, R. & Kasl, S. (1996). Gender, marital closeness, and depressive symptoms in elderly couples. *Journal of Gerontology: Psychological Sciences,* 51 (3), 115-129.

Treboux, D., Crowell, J. & Waters, E. (2004). When "new" meets "old": Configurations of adult attachment representations and their implications for marital functioning. *Developmental Psychology,* 40 (2), 295-314.

Trinder, L., Beek, M. & Connolly, J. (2002). *Making contact: How parents and children negotiate and experience contact after divorce.* York: York Publishing Services/JRF.

Twenge, J., Campbell, W. & Foster, G. (2003). Parenthood and marital satisfaction: A meta-analytic review. *Journal of Marriage and the Family,* 65 (3), 574-583.

Unger, D., & Wandersman, L. (1998). The relationship of family and partner support to the adjustment of adolescent mothers. *Child Development,* 59, 1056-1060.

Veroff, J., Young, A. & Coon, H. (2000). The early years of marriage. In R. Milardo and S. Duck (Eds.), *Families as relationships* (pp.19-38). Chichester: Wiley.

Vinokur, A., Price, R. & Caplan, R. (1996). Hard times and hurtful partners: How financial strain affects depression and relationship satisfaction of unemployed persons and their spouses. *Journal of Personality and Social Psychology,* 71 (1), 166-179.

Wade, A. & Smart, C. (2002). *Facing family change: Children's circumstances, strategies and resources.* York: York Publishing Services/ JRF.

Wade, T. & Prevalin, D. (2004). Marital transitions and mental health. *Journal of Health and Social Behaviour,* 45 (June), 155-170.

Wadhwa, P. (2005). Psychoneuroendocrine processes in human pregnancy influence fetal development and health. *Psychoneuroendocrinology,* 30 (8) 724–743.

Wadhwa, P., Sandman, C. & Garite, T. (2001). The neurobiology of stress in human pregnancy: Implications for prematurity and development of the fetal central nervous system. *Progress in Brain Research,* 133, 131–142.

Waite, L. & Luo, Y. (2002). *Marital happiness and marital stability: Consequences for psychological well-being.* Paper presented at the meetings of the American Sociological Association, August, Chicago.

Weinberg, T. & Vogler, C. (1990). Wives of alcoholics: Stigma management and adjustments to husband-wife interactions. *Deviant Behaviour,* 11, 331-343.

Weissman, M. (1987). Advances in psychiatric epidemiology: Rates and risks for major depression. *American Journal of Public Health,* 77 (4), 445-451.

Welsh, E., Buchanan, A., Flouri, E. & Lewis, J. (2004). *Fathers' involvement: A study of resident and non-resident fathers with teenage children.* London: National Children's Bureau/ Joseph Rowntree Foundation.

Werner, E. & Smith, R. (1989). *Vulnerable but invincible.* New York: Adams, Bannister and Cox.

Werner, E. & Smith, R. (1992). *Overcoming the odds: High risk children from birth to adulthood.* Ithaca, NY: Cornel University Press.

Werner, E. & Smith, R. (2001). *Journeys from childhood to midlife.* Ithaca, NY,:Cornell University Press.

Whisman, M. (2001). Depression and marital distress: Findings from clinical and community studies. In S. Beach (Ed.), *Marital and family processes in depression* (pp.3-24). Washington, DC: American Psychological Association.

Whisman, M., Dixon, A. & Johnson, B. (1997). Therapists' perspectives of couple problems and treatment issues in couple therapy. *Journal of Family Psychology,* 11 (3), 361-366.

Wiegner, S. & Donders, J. (2000). Predictors of parental distress after congenital disabilities. *Journal of Developmental and Behavioural Pediatrics,* 21 (4), 271-277.

Wilcox, B. & Nock, S. (2006). What's love got to do with it? Equality, equity, commitment and women's marital quality. *Social Forces,* 84 (3), 1321-1345.

Wile, D. (1988). *How conflict can improve your relationship.* New York: Wiley.

Wilkie, J., Feree, M. & Ratcliff, K. (1998). Gender and fairness: Marital satisfaction in two-earner couples. *Journal of Marriage and the Family,* 60 (3), 577-594.

Women's Aid (2008). *Domestic Violence: Frequently Asked Questions Factsheet.* (Retrieved August 2008 www.womensaid.org.uk).

YouGov (2008). Cited in *Breakthrough Britain: The next generation.* London: Centre for Social Justice.

Notes